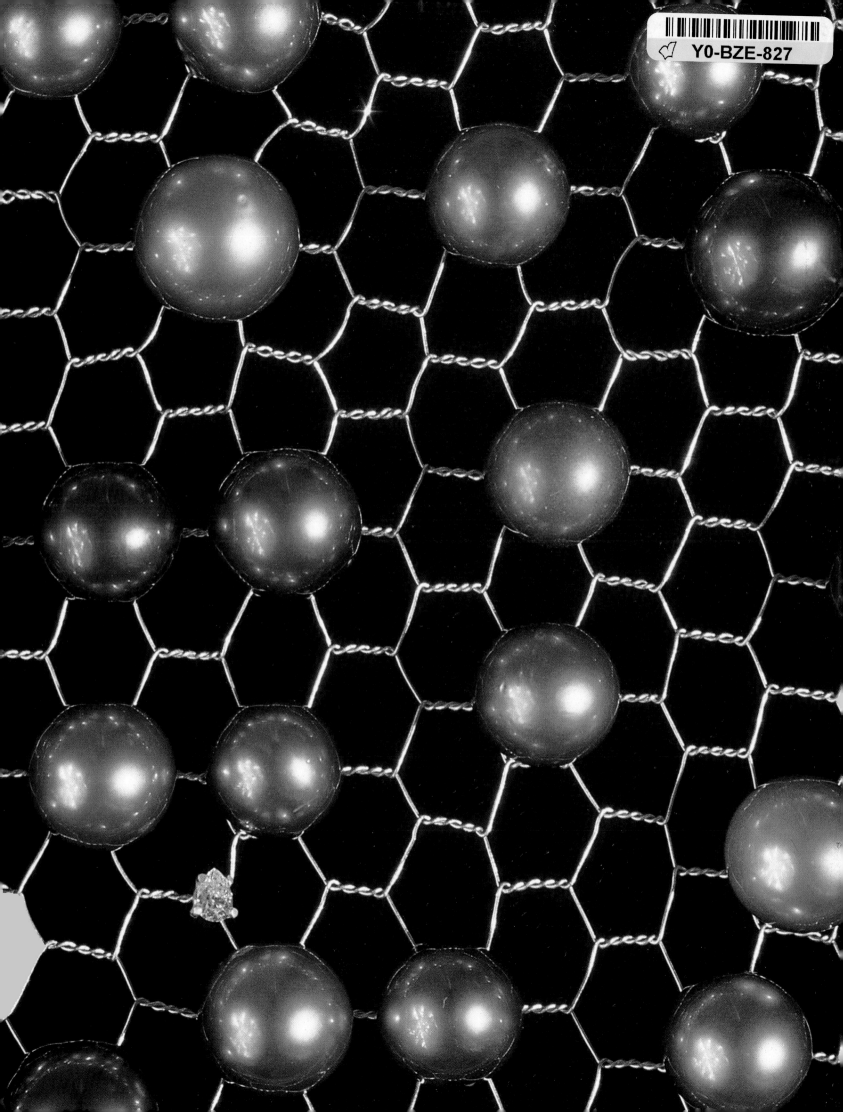

This book should be of interest to all those who love pearls for their beauty, those who are potential buyers and owners, and those who are professional dealers in pearl jewelry. The book tells all you need to know about the black pearls of Polynesia:

- Their history
- How they are produced
- Their characteristics
- How to evaluate pearls for beauty and price
- How pearls are used as jewelry

Black pearls of TAHITI

Translated from the French by Jean L. Sherman

Text by **Dr. Jean-Paul Lintilhac**
Photographs by **Alain Durand**

© Copyright of text: Jean-Paul Lintilhac, M.D.
© Copyright of photographs: Alain Durand (*)
All rights reserved under international copyright.

Page layout: Alain Durand
Book design: Arlette Deligny of Polytram Tahiti
Printing and lithography: Marchesi Grafiche Editoriali, Roma
                     Via Fabbriche di Vallico, 23 - Tel. 06/5220495-5237834

Published by Royal Tahitian Pearl Book, B.P. 2645, Papeete, Tahiti
Printed in Rome, Italy, June 1987
Copyrighted in third quarter 1985
The arrangement of black pearls on a grid of 24 carat gold, shown on the end papers of this book,
was created by Giovanni Onorato, Milan.

(*) See page 107 for a list of photographs covered by separate copyright.

Publisher N° 2-9502024
I.S.B.N. 2-9502024-1-1 for english version.
Printed in Italy.

Preface

Woman, beauty, aesthetics, and research...

These terms inevitably come to mind when I think of this remarkable work on the pearls of Polynesia and of its author, Dr. Jean-Paul Lintilhac, famous the world over for his dedication to feminine beauty in the field of cosmetic surgery.

Because of his own personal interest in the subject, Dr. Lintilhac undertook this study of one of the most exciting adventures of our time: the development of the cultured pearl. The growth of a pearl begins with a surgical intervention and ends with a work of art, an incomparable jewel taken from the sea to adorn and enhance "l'éternel féminin."

Grown chiefly in Polynesia, the PINCTADA MARGARITIFERA oyster and its CUMINGI variant are the source of the Polynesian cultured pearls whose natural color ranges from a delicate pearl gray to that brilliant green-black specific to the "poe rava." Their like is not found anywhere else in the world. They vary in shape, the most sought after being the round pearls that are seldom less than eight millimeters in diameter. None of the imitation pearls produced elsewhere can be compared to the brilliant, inimitable pearls of Polynesia.

The Government of Polynesia has taken steps to protect the existing oyster beds and will spare no effort to maintain the quality of pearl production, which by 1983 had become Polynesia's leading export.

The purpose of Dr. Lintilhac's well documented book is to extend our knowledge of black pearls so that we may love and appreciate them to the fullest. Henceforth it will serve as a reference work on the black pearl, that symbol of Polynesian wealth and beauty.

ALEXANDRE LÉONTIEFF
*Vice President of the Government
of French Polynesia
Minister of the Economy, Planning,
Tourism, Industry, Foreign Trade,
and the Sea*

Acknowledgements

For the assistance given me during the preparation of this book, I would like to express my appreciation to:

My wife, who helped with the research and writing.

My friend, Sadao Ishibashi, a Japanese grafting expert who revealed to me the secrets of his technique and gave me the benefit of his long experience throughout the South Seas.

Various government services who have always been most willing to provide information and documentation. Special thanks to:

EVAAM (Aquatic & Maritime Service) whose director, Monsieur Galenon, gave me the benefit of his advice. EVAAM's remarkable technical papers prepared under the direction of Monsieur Coeroli were one of my main sources of information.

CNEXO (National Center for Maritime Research), where Monsieur Coatanea made me welcome during my early research on pearl oysters and provided abundant and precious documentation.

The Museum of Tahiti and Her Islands, whose curator, Mlle. Manouche Lehartel, kindly allowed us to photograph some of the rare old objects in the museum and gave me her personal assistance in establishing a bibliography.

OPATTI (the Tahiti Tourist Board), which gave me access to documents, photographs, and maps.

Koko Chaze, beginning in 1972, who allowed me to visit the S.P.M. (Manihi Pearl Company) and to watch Professor Wada operating on the oysters. Koko helped me with documentation and with his personal comments.

Totie Garnier of Polynesie Perles, who gave me the benefit of her vast knowledge of the pearl market.

Giovanni Onorato, Via della Spiga, Milano, for his valuable contribution in the illustration of this book.

Dr. Pierre Amalric for his kindness in sharing with us his library where books are like rare pearls.

Stefano Marchesi and his team at Marchesi Grafiche Editoriali di Roma to whom we give credit for the successful completion of this work.

U.T.A., Air France and Air Polynesia Airlines.

Marcia Aubineau-Lintilhac for her help and participation.

My thanks as well to all the people who helped me, each in his or her own way, to a better knowledge and appreciation of the black pearls of Tahiti.

The black pearls of Tahiti

"Black pearls of Tahiti" is the customary term, but as you read this book and learn that these pearls don't come from Tahiti and seldom are black, you may decide that it is a misnomer. The so-called black pearls actually are grown in some of the outer islands of French Polynesia, particularly in the Tuamotu Archipelago and the Gambier Islands.

Tahiti itself is the main island of French Polynesia, the seat of government and administrative services, the center of economic activity and one of legend. Her name alone is enough to stir the imagination of anyone who has read Pierre Loti, Robert Louis Stevenson, Charles Nordhoff and James Norman Hall, or fled the humdrum of daily life via one of Gauguin's paintings. In brochures filled with color photographs and stereotypical prose, Tahiti still beckons to people starved for sunshine and eager for escape.

It may be helpful if we describe the geographical location of Tahiti and the other islands of French Polynesia.

As for the pearls, their colors range from shimmering white through the variations of steel gray, bronze, blue, green, purple, pink, even copper and gold, all the way to luminous black. They can be round, button-shaped or pear-shaped, baroque, circled, blister or keshis - terms which this book will help you understand.

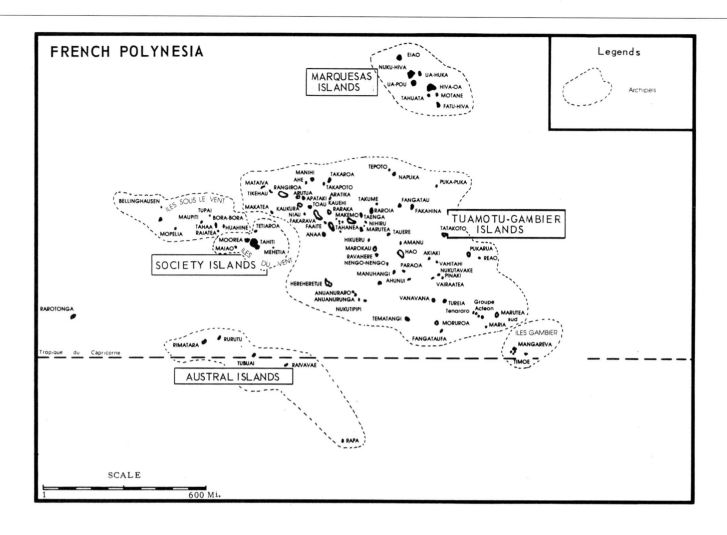

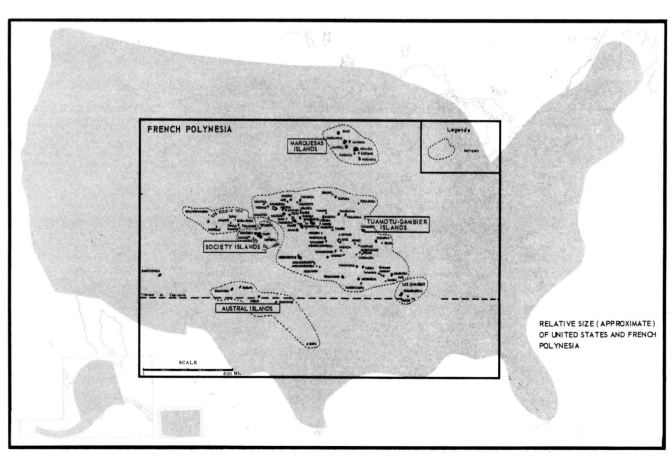

RELATIVE SIZE (APPROXIMATE) OF UNITED STATES AND FRENCH POLYNESIA

A few facts about French Polynesia

GEOGRAPHICALLY SPEAKING

Tahiti is the largest island in French Polynesia, which is in the South Pacific about midway between California and Australia, equi-distant from Santiago, Chile, and Tokyo, Japan. French Polynesia occupies an area equal to that of Europe, not including Russia, but the actual land surface totals only 4,000 square kilometers (about 2,500 square miles). It comprises 130 islands divided into five archipelagoes: the Society Islands, which include the Windward Islands (Tahiti, Moorea, Maiao) and the Leeward Islands or Iles Sous le Vent (Bora Bora, Huahine, Raiatea, Tahaa), the Tuamotu Archipelago, Gambiers and Australes.

All these islands are of volcanic origin and built by coral. We can distinguish between the high islands which have a mountain of volcanic origin in the center and are surrounded by a coral reef which encloses a lagoon, and the low islands or atolls where the original central mountain has sunk (as described by Darwin's theory of subsidence), leaving only a coral reef that surrounds an inner lagoon. Tahiti, which has an area of 1000 square kilometers (about 600 square miles), is an extraordinarily beautiful islands with luxurious vegetation. The island is dominated by two peaks: Orohena (altitude 2,235 meters or approximately 7,100 feet) and Aorai (altitude 2,066 meters or approximately 6,200 feet).

HOW'S THE CLIMATE?

Tahiti is cooled by the Pacific tradewinds, making the climate sunny and pleasant. There are two seasons: December to February, which is hot and humid, with temperatures ranging from 27 to 35 C. (80 to 92 F.), and March to November which is cooler and dryer, with temperatures between 21° and 27° C. (70° to 80° F.). Most of the rainfall occurs during the hot season, December to March.

WHAT TIME IS IT?

When it is noon on Sunday in Tahiti, it is:
Sunday
  2 P.M. in Los Angeles
  4 P.M. in Chicago and Mexico City
  5 P.M. in New York and Lima, Peru
  6 P.M. in Caracas, Venezuela and
          Santiago, Chile
  7 P.M. in Buenos Aires, Montevideo
          and Rio de Janeiro
10 P.M. in London
11 P.M. in Paris, Frankfurt, Madrid
          and Rome
Monday
10 A.M. in Auckland and Fiji
  8 A.M. in Sydney and Melbourne
  7 A.M. in Tokyo
  6 A.M. in Hong Kong
Midnight in Johannesburg

HOW FAR IS TAHITI?

From:
London and Paris: 18,000 km (10,800 miles)
Los Angeles and Santiago, Chile: 8,000 km (4,800 miles)
Auckland, New Zealand: 4,100 km (2,500 miles)
Sydney, Australia: 6,700 km (4,020 miles)
Tokyo, Japan: 9,500 km (5,700 miles)

WHAT'S THE POPULATION?

According to an estimate made in January 1984, French Polynesia has 167,200 inhabitants, more than half of whom live in Tahiti. Papeete, capital of the territory, has approximately 24,000 inhabitants. The population is made up of Polynesians of Maori origin, 75%; Orientals, 10%; and Europeans, 15%. Tahitians are known for their beauty, hospitality and happy dispositions. There are two official languages, French and Tahitian, but almost everyone in the tourist industry also speaks English.

History of the pearl oysters and pearls of Polynesia

I. THE OLD DAYS FROM THE DISCOVERY OF TAHITI UNTIL 1960

Pearls have been known and valued in both the Orient and the Western world from earliest times. Curiously enough, however, they did not appear upon the scene in Polynesia until the arrival of European navigators in the seventeenth and eighteenth centuries.

Polynesian museums contain jewelry, as well as utilitarian objects such as fishhooks and fishing lures, made from the magnificent local oyster shells (commonly called "nacre" in French) that are the source of mother-of-pearl. Typically, mother-of-pearl was used to decorate ceremonial costumes, such as those worn by the chief mourners at a funeral.

Wallis, Bougainville and Cook all left records of their voyages of exploration in the Pacific, yet none of them mentions the pearls which must have embellished the breast ornaments and headdresses of the numerous native chiefs. This oversight is all the more surprising because the expeditionary captains, especially those from Holland, were well aware of the commercial nature of their discoveries. In April 1722 Roggeveen, advised his men to "look closely at the jewelry worn by the islanders, since this is the easiest and quickest way to learn whether gold, precious stones or pearls are to be found in the Islands."

A man named Banks who was a member of Cook's first expedition brought back an etching with portraits of several women from Tahiti and the Leeward Islands (Iles Sous le Vent). He comments that they used to wear flowers or pearls in holes pierced in their earlobes. The pearls were placed in a little net made of strands of hair woven together.

Pearls were also used to represent the eyes in some of the sculptures of Hawaii Kukailimoku,

the god of war, as shown in etchings in Cook's account of his voyage. These are the only two examples I have found of pearls being used at the time the explorers arrived in Tahiti.

And yet during this time the navigators were forever looking for pearls and pearl oysters. When Roggeveen discovered Easter Island, he noted that the inhabitants wore silver discs in their ears and pendants of mother-of-pearl. His voyage continued until one of his ships, the Africaansche Galey, was wrecked on the coral reefs of Takapoto. Karl Friedrich Behrens, a member of that expedition, says of Takapoto in his journal: "We also found there many mussels, shells and pearl oysters, so many that it seemed likely that one might establish a profitable pearl fishery — the more so because we found pearls in a few of the oysters that the natives had pulled off the rocks."

There may be a simple explanation for the fact that pearls were not used in Tahitian jewelry before the arrival of the Europeans: the natives had no metals and therefore did not possess tools sharp enough or hard enough to pierce pearls. Likewise, the glue used in those days, which probably was made from the sap of the

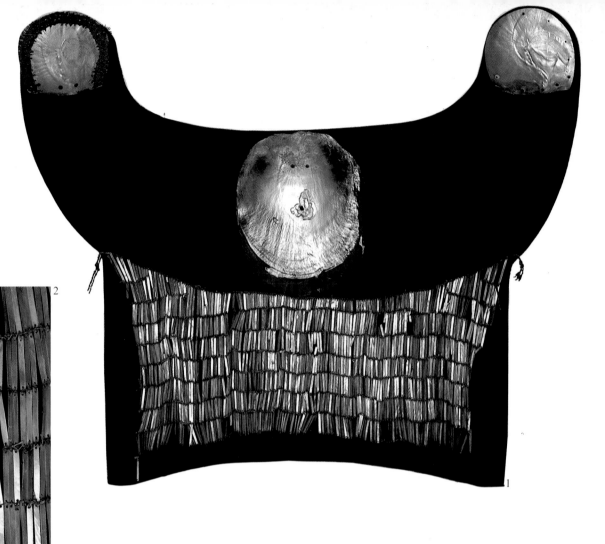

1 - Portion of a mourning garment made of mother-of-pearl. (M.T.I. 78.03-52, 78.03-53, 78.03-54).

2 - Detail of mourning garment.

3 - Sculptured Maori wooden panel (lintel of a community house). (M.T.I. 59).

4 - Detail of Maori panel: eye inlaid with haliotide shell.

5 - Point of a shell lure used for bonita fishing. Three shell fishhooks. (Site de FA'AHIA-HUAHINE).

6 - Ornament of small toothed oyster shell strung on plaited fiber. (TUAMOTU - M.T.I. 78.03-57).

7 - Chest ornament hung from strands of plaited hair attached by a coconut leaf. (AUSTRALES - M.T.I. 80.04-47).

Collection of the MUSEUM OF TAHITI AND ITS ISLANDS.

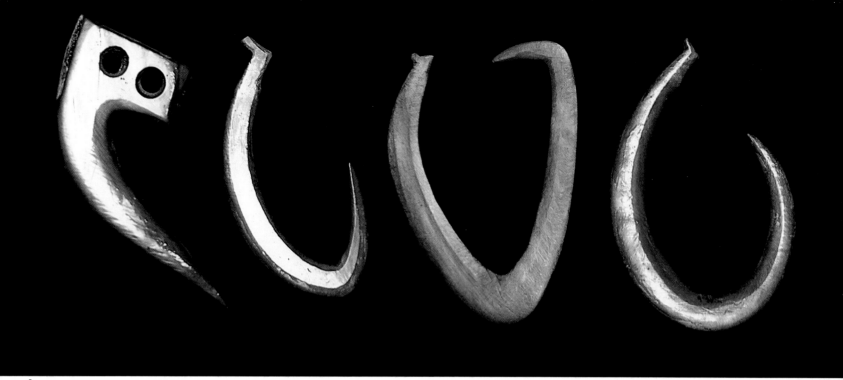

5

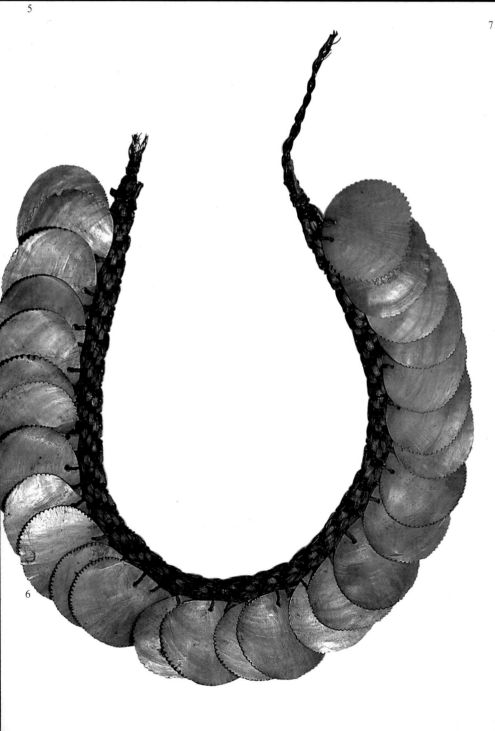

6

7

ARRIVAL DATES
OF THE FIRST NAVIGATORS
FROM EUROPE
AND SOUTH AMERICA

1521 The Portuguese Magellan discovered Puka Puka, an uninhabited island in the extreme northwest of the Tuamotus.

1595 Mendona, a Spaniard, who sailed from Peru in search of the "Terra Australis," discovered Fatuhiva, the most southerly of the Marquesas.

1606 Quiros, another Spaniard also sailing from Peru, after sighting several uninhabited atolls, disembarked at Hao, then crossed the eastern Tuamotus and finally reached the New Hebrides, where he founded "New Jerusalem" on the island of Santo.

1616 Two Dutchmen, Le Maire and Schouten, first discovered Takaroa, then Takapoto and Manihi, where they were driven off by flies.

1722 On April 5, Roggeveen, another Dutchman, discovered Easter Island and later sighted Tikei before one of his ships went aground on the reefs of Takapoto. He just missed Manihi and Apataki, glimpsed Arutua and Rangiroa, went ashore at Makatea, then discovered Bora Bora and Maupiti.

1767 The English navigator Samuel Wallis brought his ship *Dolphin* to Nukutavake, sailed by Mehetia and was the first to discover Tahiti on June 19, 1767.

1768 The famous French captain, Bougainville, passed by Hao, crossed the Tuamotus, and reached Tahiti.

1769 Captain James Cook landed on Tahiti for the first time.

1

2

3

4

uru or breadfruit tree, was not strong enough to bear the weight of pearls.

Later it was reported that one of the Queens Pomare played marbles with pearls, and in all probability pearls were used in the same fashion in earlier times.

After the discovery of Tahiti, trading in pearls and mother-of-pearl developed very quickly. About 1825 Beechy, on the Blossom, rediscovered the Gambier Archipelago, more specifically, Mangareva. From 1830 on, trading ships called regularly at Mangareva. At least two such ships belonged to French navigators based at Valparaiso, while others came from Botany Bay in Australia. Sons of English missionaries sailed from Tahiti soon thereafter to collect pearls and mother-of-pearl. Some of these ships began to bring divers from the Tuamotus and from Rapa; this led to quarrels and even bloody battles between the newcomers and the Mangarevans.

In the early days a man had only to stand waist-deep in the water to pick up pearl oysters, but by 1850 Moerenhout reported that they were beginning to be scarce. Of the inhabitants of Mangareva, he wrote: "They still have coconuts and fish, and before their oyster banks were destroyed, they had a means of subsistence that was both certain and easy to reach. But today the oysters are less common; one can find them only at great depths. Now the natives will either have to work harder at cultivating the land or go hungry." From this it appears that, first and foremost, the pearl oysters were a source of food and by 1834 excessive harvesting had seriously reduced the oyster supply.

In 1836 when the French navigator Dumont D'Urville visited Mangareva, everyone on board kept a journal. Here is what Captain Jacquinot of the Zélée had to say:

The captains who have visited these islands in order to buy pearls concede that the missionaries have done the natives a great deal of good. The captains recognize the hard work the missionaries do each day and the many privations they endure for the sole purpose of civilizing and improving the natives.

But as traders who look first to their own interests, they accuse the missionaries of having ruined commerce and upset their profits.

Before the missionaries came, the captains say that a knife, a fishhook or some beads could be exchanged for quite a beautiful pearl. To-

1 - *Louis Antoine de Bougainville, who between 1766 and 1769 circumnavigated the globe on the frigate* La Boudeuse, *escorted by* L'Etoile.

2 - Adventure, *Captain James Cook's ship on his second voyage around the world (1772-1775).*

3 - *Captain Cook. In the course of his three voyages (1768-1780) he mapped a large part of the Pacific. His explorations reached from Alaska and the west coast of Canada to the Hawaiian Islands, Tahiti, the Society Islands, the Marquesas, New Caledonia, and Easter Island.*

4 - *Painting by William Hodges of* Resolution *and* Adventure *in Matavai Bay, Tahiti.*

5 - *Dumont d'Urville.*

6 - *Captain Cook accepting gifts from the natives.*

6

J.S.C. DUMONT D'URVILLE,
Commandant l'Expédition de l'Astrolabe,

5

day they are obliged to give 20 or 30 measures of Indian cotton for the same article. To which the missionaries reply, "Then why do you come back? Your regular trips to this area prove that in spite of your complaints, your profits are immense. You are angry only because we have taught these simple souls to cover themselves and to know the value of their merchandise."

Besides, what has done most to increase the value of the pearls is the competition among the traders. To corner the market, they raise their bids. The natives know very well how to turn this to their advantage.

Cesar Desgraz, Commander Dumont D'Urville's secretary, wrote as follows about a Breton named Guillou who had settled in Mangareva:

Guillou has his own oyster fishery and has set the ordinary wage for a diver at one measure of rough cotton per week, but this salary is less sought after than it used to be. The divers want more and Guillou will soon have to raise them or get along without their services.

During the fishing season, which takes place particularly during the calm weather in January when the divers can see the oysters better in the deep water, a successful week would result in one barrel of oysters per diver. On an average, this yields an ounce of small and medium-sized pearls for which the price in Valparaiso is now between 60 and 80 francs, not counting the mother-of-pearl of the shells which likewise can be sold at a good price. One can weigh this information given by Guillou against the chance of finding really beautiful pearls, which bring a higher price and can yield an incalculable profit. Such possibilities are rare, however, and Guillou complains of the morals of the natives, who are paid a salary but know which oysters have large pearls and hide them and keep them for themselves. King Mapouteoa, since he knows the value of these pearls, takes them from his subjects by his authority as their sovereign when he learns they have one of good size and clarity.

It is worth noting that all the "official" explorers categorized the ship captains who traded for pearls and mother-of-pearl as speculators and profiteers who became outrageously wealthy. While this may be true, we must not forget the enormous risks that the captains ran, sailing among coral atolls in those uncharted seas. Because the atolls lie very low in the water and are difficult to see, these waters are still dangerous today. We might mention two examples.

The good ship Josephine, which the above mentioned Guillou left (or deserted) in Mangareva, was wrecked in the Fiji Islands; her captain, Antoine Bureau, and all his crew were massacred.

Likewise the Sarah Ann in 1856 had the misfortune to run aground on Tematangi atoll; her entire company, including the captain's wife and an infant of 22 months, was eaten by the inhabitants. We should remember as well the financial risks run by the shipowners, many of whose vessels never returned to their home ports.

In 1871 the author Gardarein-Freytet assessed the pearl situation and concluded that the profits were less than people supposed.

He wrote as follows about the Gambier Islands: *As for the pearl trade, in 1861 Mr. Duprat, commander of the brig Le Railleur, estimated it at 20,000 francs, according to information given to him personally in the Gambiers.*

Personally I believe that figure is much too high. Other notes and documents on the pearl trade, including the pearls sent as gifts to King Louis Philippe I, lead us to estimate the annual value of that trade at around 11,000 francs.

Pearls are not produced with any degree of regularity; therefore, many years must be taken into account in order to arrive at an annual figure that is accurate. For that reason I have worked with all the figures available from 1844 to 1864.

The average person considers pearls an easy source of fabulous wealth. He imagines that the Tuamotu and Gambier Islands, which produce the pearl oyster, are a sort of Mother Lode that can be exploited indefinitely. The facts of the matter are quite different. The Mangareva Islands, which constitute one fifth of this trade, can produce 75 or 80 tons of good mother-of-pearl every year. A larger quantity cannot be taken without risking the immediate exhaustion of the banks.

In 1856 and 1857, for instance, considerably more than 80 tons were harvested. In the years that followed, the impoverishment of the oyster banks was so evident that in 1862, it was necessary to stop the fishing. This interruption continued for four years, but unfortunately the amount levied on Tahiti by France prevented an extension of the ban beyond that initial period.

Values different from those quoted above have been given for the annual trade in the Gambiers. Some people have estimated the commerce in pearls at 200,000 francs a year, but this figure is totally without foundation. The trade never reached such heights, not even in 1857 when 375 tons of oysters — that is, five times as much as can reasonably be expected — were harvested and sold. The first lot of mother-of-pearl weighed 200 tons and was paid for in merchandise. The second lot weighed 171 tons and was paid for in money which the buyers themselves estimated at 185,625 francs. From that must be subtracted the difference between the actual price of the merchandise and its value as estimated by the European merchants.

From the time the first navigators arrived until about 1860, the harvesting and trading of oysters and pearls were entirely in the hands of the captains of trading vessels, who operated essentially according to a barter system.

There were no official controls.

Beginning in 1860 the government intervened more and more to regulate oyster and pearl fishing, which had become a real industry.

Diving for pearl oysters
Old Style (1860-1960)

The term diving is used here in its true sense. No longer was oyster fishing a matter of standing waist-deep in the sea or simply diving into shallow water to pick up the oysters. Now the divers had to descend to depths of 20 to 30 meters (approximately 60 to 90 feet) to harvest the precious crop.

A few days before the season opened, the divers would arrive by boat, often accompanied by their families. The boats also carried all of their equipment: ropes, outrigger canoes, etc. With the divers came an influx of traders, prospective buyers of pearls and mother-of-pearl, and vendors of various kinds, creating a country fair atmosphere. Later the government also sent its representatives — postal clerks, gendarmes, and officials of the Department of Fisheries.

In 1880 an average diver earned between 120 and 150 francs a month[1] — sometimes more if the oysters were abundant. Diving would begin at about 7 a.m. when, after a prayer service, the boat (or a group of outriggers towed by a boat) would go out to the oyster banks. The divers wore a *pareu* or Tahitian loincloth and had with them a *lunette* or sort of glass-bottom box that allowed them to look under water and see the oysters at a considerable depth. After examining the bottom, a diver would hold onto a big rock tied to a rope and would go down, then feel out and collect the oysters he had seen from the surface.

About this time some of the traders tried to convert the Paumotus (the inhabitants of the Tuamotus) to diving suits. The diving equipment of that time was very heavy, consisting as it did of weighted boots, a rubber suit, and a copper helmet with a porthole in front for visibility, with the whole outfit connected to the boat above by a tube through which air was constantly pumped. Although some Europeans used the diving suits successfully, the Polynesians never were able to adapt completely to the cumbersome apparatus.

They claimed the suits caused a kind of palsy in their legs. In any case, diving suits were soon forbidden because they were considered risky and because they didn't allow the divers to compete on an equal footing.

In January 1903, when the lagoon of Hikueru

Pearl diver, old style, wearing wooden goggles.

---

[1] *A civil servant, an assistant of the Governor, earned 700 francs per month in the year 1900.*

Island had just been opened for pearl fishing, a cyclone devastated the Tuamotus. The population of the island had previously jumped from 400 to 1250 — an indication of the number of people accompanying the oyster divers to a rich location newly available for exploitation. When the cyclone was over, there were 377 dead, 80 cutters and 800 outrigger canoes destroyed. Following this cyclone, many new lagoons were opened to pearl fishing, and diving suits were temporarily authorized to allow the Tuamotus to recoup their losses. As a result, in 1903 and 1904 the oyster harvest doubled.

Only a few of the Paumotus were in business for themselves as pearl fishers. Most of them had neither the money nor the ambition for such a venture. Some would hire out by the day on fishing boats; others would sign up for a season with a merchant from Papeete or with a captain in business for himself on the inter-island waters.

After 1910 the divers had a new device that helped them greatly: a pair of spectacles made of wood or copper and fitted with glass — something like the goggles worn by today's racing swimmers. Such glasses were not comfortable in deep water but did allow the divers better underwater vision.

Diving began to be better organized. The divers went out two per outrigger, accompanied by an assistant. Each diver had a 50 meter (150 foot) rope to which were attached an oyster basket and a lead weight weighing eight kilograms (17.5 pounds). After taking several deep breaths, the diver would dive, holding the weight between his feet to help him get to the bottom. There he would pull up the oyster, which was attached to the coral by its byssus (a set of filaments secreted by a gland in the foot of the oyster). Detaching it wasn't always an easy job, especially if the byssus happened to be anchored in a crevice, preventing the diver from pulling it loose with his usual twisting movement. Once detached, the oysters were placed in the basket which the assistant then would pull up, after which he would help the diver return to the surface.

The Paumotus were and are very skillful divers. After a training period in which they plunged no deeper than 20 meters (60 feet), they were able to go down 30 or 40 meters and remain from a minute and a half to three minutes. They were able to continue diving in that fashion from 7 a.m. to 3 p.m., making 50 to 80 dives per day.

At about three o'clock, diving would stop. The diver would then use a large knife to open the oyster wide so that its flesh could be examined and probed in search of a pearl. Unless the muscle was intended for that evening's stew, it was impaled on a wire and left to dry; however, it usually didn't remain there long because everyone who walked by would help himself to a piece of this tempting delicacy.

And the oyster wasn't the only temptation. Boat captains had to keep a sharp eye on their workmen, who were known to quickly swallow a fine pearl if they found one.

Small pearls were still found quite often, but unfortunately the big beautiful pearls were becoming more and more rare. Big pearls grow in old oysters, and with the heavy diving schedules, old oysters were hard to find, even though a four year ban on diving was imposed after each fishing season.

Large pearls were quite common until 1850 or so; after that the percentage diminished. By 1960 divers were having to look at about 100,000 oysters to find one good-sized pearl. It began to seem that the game was worth neither its cost nor the considerable risks run by the divers.

In the middle twenties a man named Leonard Rosenthal, who was known in Paris as "the pearl king," wrote a book called *In the Pearl Kingdom*. He described the life of the divers as follows:

In all pearl fishing areas life is hard: always the same tropical heat, the same lack of water, the same risk of illness. Every two or three years there is an outbreak of sickness: plague and cholera in Bahrein, yellow fever in Panama and South America, and dysentery everywhere.

It is only by observing the strictest rules of hygiene that Europeans manage to preserve their health. Life is not very pleasant anywhere: there is only the sea, the burnt sands in the sun, and not a bit of greenery in the landscape. Food is canned, and often spoiled by the heat. It's pointless to talk about comfort: the native customs are too primitive and rough.

To top it off, in all the fisheries the oysters that are exposed to air rot very quickly, giving off a foul stench and noxious miasma. To cover up the smell, everyone smokes excessively — which in itself is a menace to health.

The Dangers of Pearl Diving

Without being so dramatic, we can agree that the life of a Paumotu diver (and those who work with him) has never been all that nice. In addition to the lack of comfort, mosquito and "no-see-em" bites, heat and sunburn, diving can be dangerous.

Although everyone is aware of the risks of decompression when a diving suit or aqualung is used, free diving at frequent intervals and to great depths may also involve accidents and complications, both then and now. Most often it is the diver's ears that are at risk; burst eardrums and progressive loss of hearing are common. Sinusitis is another frequent complaint.

The most serious accident is underwater blackout, usually followed by drowning. This happens several times each year to visiters to Polynesia — people who are in good general physical condition but don't spend enough time training and adapting their bodies to the rigors of free diving. Professional free divers who exceed the limits of their considerable strength are also subject to such attacks.

The greatest long-term risk, however, is *tara-vana* (the Tahitian word for madness), a sort of "folie douce" characterized by mild mental problems.

There are other exterior dangers to which the pearl diver is exposed, the most common being coral cuts on the hands, arms and legs.

Coral wounds must be thoroughly cleansed to remove any coral fragments and they are slow to heal.

Salt water tends to enlarge the wounds; localized infections accompanied by inflamed glands are frequent. Even if the wound is only a scratch, some corals are so irritating that mere contact with them can provoke a painful skin reaction.

Another danger comes from certain fish, such as stone fish and dragon fish, which are poisonous; their stings are very painful and may even cause a state of shock that can be fatal. A kind of starfish (called *taramea* in Tahitian) that attacks the coral is also extremely poisonous. The moray eel is dangerous as well, and its bite is very painful. At least the masks now available give the divers clear vision and allow them, with a minimum of care, to avoid these creatures.

As for sharks, they were likewise more of a peril when divers didn't have today's high quality masks. Literature is full of shark stories, but in the lagoons of the Tuamotu and Gambier Islands at the present time, sharks no longer constitute a real danger. In view of that, what Bouchon-Brandely wrote in 1885 on the subject of sharks strikes us today as rather amusing:

What dangers await the unlucky divers when they explore the dark depths of the lagoon where the hungry sharks rule as kings! Who knows whether they will return mutilated from those depths, or, better, whether they will not stay there entombed forever. Voracious and ravenous, the sharks patrol the fishing grounds, hoping to find a prey. It's a permanent state of menace.

In spite of all his agility and watchfulness, the diver cannot escape them, he is condemned to a terrible and unequal combat. Among many examples, I mention the case of a woman from Anaa whose breast and arm were torn off by one of these fearful sea wolves.

When an accident of that kind occurs, terror spreads among the diving population. Diving then stops for a certain time because no one is willing to run the risks. But this well-deserved feeling of fear doesn't last long, because the divers must earn their daily bread. However, in truth, spear fishermen must take care not to tow dead or wounded fish around with them, and they should be alert to a threatening attitude on the part of a shark or the formation of a shark pack.

Production of mother-of-pearl

After falling off between 1930 and 1940, the production of mother-of-pearl held steady at around 500 tons a year until 1960.

This curve, taken from *Present Knowledge of the Lagoon Environment* ("Milieu lagonaire - Etat de Connaissance," EVAAM, 1983), illustrates the sizeable drop in production that occurred between 1960 and 1963, at the time when Faaa International Airport and the Center for Atomic Experimentation in the

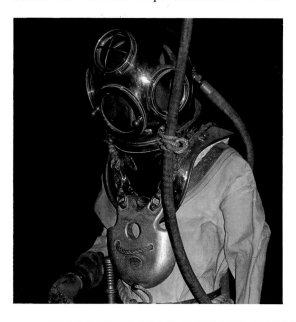

Deep-sea diver wearing diving suit.

Pacific were built. Because of the high wages paid, those two projects attracted many people from the outer islands.

Another reason for the downward curve is a reduction in the number of pearl oysters, which diminishes every year. Mother-of-pearl is less in demand; the supply on hand doesn't sell.

Fishing for pearl oysters has become less productive and less profitable, and natural black pearls are practically not to be found anymore.

Therefore the people in Tahiti who didn't want to abandon this sector of activity had to look for another solution.

Already in 1885, Bouchon-Brandely, secretary of the College de France, sent to Tahiti by the Marine and Colonial Ministry to study oyster and pearl fisheries, observed the impoverishment of the lagoons and advocated the collection of the spats as well as the regulation of the fishing season, including a strict prohibition of fishing on certain oyster banks so that they could renew themselves. He also proposed collecting the spats.

Simon Grand, an oyster breeder from Arcachon on the Atlantic coast of France, settled in the Gambier Islands where he collected spats of the *Pinctada margaritifera* oyster and recommended the use of the *miki miki*, a native bush, in collector baskets (explained in Chapter 2.) Lack of government funding interrupted Grand's experiments, but he remained in Tahiti and became the founder of a large Tahitian family.

Others followed in the footsteps of those two: Professor Seurat, Captain Wilmet, Francois Herve, administrator of the Tuamotus, and, in 1953, Professor Gilbert Ranson of the Museum of Natural History in Paris. All these distinguished civil servants worked on the theoretical side of the mother-of-pearl industry, but none of them had the persistence or the drive — or perhaps the profit motive — to put their theories into practice.

In the early part of the twentieth century the situation of the pearl oyster was worrisome but by 1962 it had become catastrophic.

Whereas between 1899 and 1908 the export rate for mother-of-pearl was only 300 to 600 tons a year, between 1950 and 1960 super-exploitation of the oysters drove it up to 500 to 850 tons a year. Thanks to conservation measures enforced by the Department of Fisheries and also to the law of supply and demand, the pessimists who for more than a century (according to Moerenhout, 1834) had predicted the complete extinction of the pearl oyster were proved wrong. However, it wasn't the mother-of-pearl trade that saved the pearl oyster, since the demand for that substance had fallen off world-wide; rather it was the pearls themselves.

Graph showing exploitation of the pearl oyster in French Polynesia from 1889 to 1981. 1940-1960, period of super-exploitation; 1960-1980, exhaustion of the resource followed by possible extinction. Dotted line represents production, solid line represents export. (Taken from "Present Knowledge of Lagoon Environment").

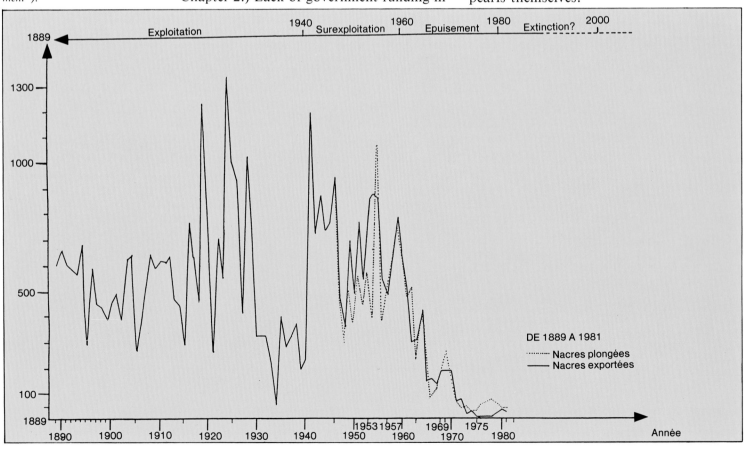

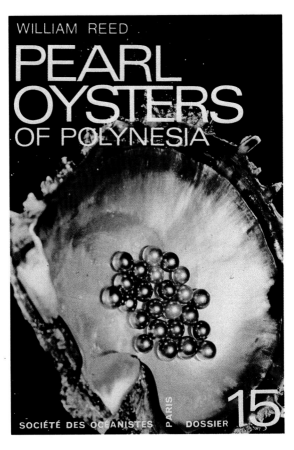

WILLIAM REED

PEARL OYSTERS OF POLYNESIA

SOCIÉTÉ DES OCÉANISTES · PARIS · DOSSIER 15

II. MODERN TIMES
(1960 to the present)

The pearls of Tahiti: from the lottery to scientific pearl culture

Natural black pearls had practically disappeared by 1960, a year in which only four or five of them were found in all of French Polynesia. It was high time, therefore, to think about producing cultured pearls.

The Chinese had known for a very long time how to provoke deposits of mother-of-pearl in certain oyster shells by placing a Sitting Buddha figurine, of lead or tin, in contact with the shell.

At the beginning of the twentieth century, the Japanese learned how to produce pearls. Kokichi Mikomoto, the great name in pearl culture, got his first five half-pearls, called mabes (pronounced ''mah-bays''), in 1893. By 1904 another Japanese, Tatsuhei, succeeded in growing the first round pearl.

In 1907 Tokichi Nishikawa perfected the technique that is still in use today, which the Japanese call the ''piece method.'' Instead of wrapping the epithelial tissue of the oyster completely around the nucleus, in the piece method only a fragment of tissue from another oyster is placed next to the nucleus.

Mikimoto produced his first round pearls in 1905, using a complete wrap technique, and later he patented the piece method.

Mikimoto was not formally trained as a scientist; he was just a tireless researcher, a dogged fighter who never gave up regardless of the obstacles confronting him, whether they were octopus invasions, red tides, cyclones or other natural disasters. He was also a born leader and a shrewd businessman who knew how to build a world-wide reputation for the Mikimoto Pearl Company. After World War II, when he was 85, he got his business back on its feet and by 1951 had approximately 20 million cultured pearls growing in his pearl farms.

Pearl culture in Polynesia

The earliest researcher in Tahiti was Bouchon-Brandely, who in 1884 undertook experiments on the *Pinctada margaritifera*. His technique — a very original one — consisted of piercing the oyster shell at different points and feeding a ball of mother-of-pearl through each hole. The tiny ball was held in place by copper wire. The holes were then sealed with a bit of wood, after which the oyster was

1 - The first cultured pearls produced in Tahiti.

2 - Koko Chaze coming up from a dive.

KOKO CHAZE, a pioneer of private enterprise

From 1966 when he began working by himself to produce half-pearls in Rangiroa to the time when, after he became local manager of the S.P.M. at Manihi where cultured pearls were produced successfully, Koko Chaze has been a leader in the development of the pearl industry in French Polynesia. For several years he had worked for the Club Med in Polynesia and other countries. Using that experience, he created in 1976 the Kaina Village (''l'Hotel du bout du monde'' — hotel at the end of the world) in Manihi. Koko is a vivacious and voluble individual (whose guests make a much more receptive audience than his pearl oysters do) — a character of sorts who describes himself as ''rude but well mannered.''

returned to the sea. A few months later, a delicate layer of mother-of-pearl would have formed around the ball. The half-pearls obtained by this method were of mediocre quality, however; no doubt the reaction between copper and salt water played an important part in the poor results of these experiments.

Toward 1960 Jean-Marie Domard, a veterinarian in charge of the Ranching and Fisheries Service, began the first serious study of ways to grow cultured pearls in Polynesia. In 1962 he brought in a Japanese specialist who grafted 5,000 oysters, and by 1965 they had obtained more than 1,000 cultured pearls of excellent quality. (A photograph of the pearls in that collection appears on the cover of *Pearl Oysters of Polynesia*.) With the help of the Department of Fisheries, some of the Paumotu people were trained in the technique of producing half-pearls, because it was easier to teach than the method of producing whole pearls and could be quickly learned.

In 1966 in Manihi atoll, two brothers, Jacques and Hubert Rosenthal — grandsons of Leonard Rosenthal, the "Pearl King" — established the first pearl farm in French Polynesia: the Societe d'Experimentation Perliere de Manihi (the SPEM, or Manihi Pearl Experimentation Company). Koko Chase, the dynamic on-site manager, received technical assistance from a Japanese specialist of the first rank, Professor Wada. By 1968 the Rosenthals had given up the idea of half-pearls and had launched a full-scale effort to produce whole pearls.

Despite the difficulties that every pioneer has to face, the SPM company prospered. It continues to prosper, although it hasn't grown as spectacularly as some farms founded later such as the one owned by Jean Claude Brouillet at South Marutea in the eastern Tuamotus and Robert Wan's farm at Mangareva. Both Brouillet and Wan are good businessmen who had already won their spurs in other markets. They didn't know much about oysters and pearls, but they had the necessary capital, they knew how to organize production and sales, and hired capable assistants.

With the help of the Department of Fisheries and the financial backing of Socredo (Société de Crédit d'Oceanie), each atoll developed its own pearl cooperative which sold its harvest of pearls at the annual auction held in Papeete. The cooperatives have been han-

JEAN-CLAUDE BROUILLET

During World War II Brouillet joined the French Resistance at the age of 16 and later was trained as a pilot in the United States. About 1950 he and his father, called "The Chief," whom I knew personally, formed an air transport company which in 1974 became Air Gabon, the national airline of that country. His book, *The White Man's Plane*, tells the story. His principal claim to fame for many people is that he married actress Marina Vlady. They had a son who today is a fine young man.

Very much attracted to Tahiti, he sold his airline and moved there. He played a leading role in the development of the Kia Ora Hotels, then bought an atoll, South Marutea, 1,500 kilometers (900 miles) from Tahiti, and threw himself into the production of black pearls — a real challenge! But he succeeded and formed a company, Polynesie Perles, a leading pearl farm.

In cooperation with Salvatore Assael, president of Assael International, he obtained certification for "natural colored black pearls" from the Gemological Institute of America. This certificate authenticates the black pearls of Tahiti and distinguishes them from dyed pearls.

Brouillet's second book, *The Black Pearl Island*, relates this adventure. However, his claim that he was the first and only producer of black pearls is questionable, and if he was the first to export black pearls to the United States, others were ahead of him in the export to Europe and Japan.

Professor Wada examines grafted oysters by X-ray and prepares to insert a nucleus.

dicapped, however, by money problems and by the uneven skills of their workers and Japanese technicians. They have had disappointing results both in profits and in the quality of their pearls. As a result, the most active members of the cooperatives often have gone into business for themselves. One now sees a number of small pearl farms run by independent Paumotus or by Paumotus who have partners in Papeete.

At present the biggest problem of the pearl farms is not producing pearls; the technique for doing that is now fairly well standardized and depends mostly on the knowledge and skill of those who do the grafting. The chief difficulty is obtaining an adequate stock of oysters.

The pearl farms: stocking, raising, and harvesting the oysters

There are two ways of obtaining stocks of pearl oysters:
1) diving for them,
2) collecting spats and raising the young oysters to maturity.

Diving new-style

Pearl diving has changed a great deal since World War II and especially since the mid-sixties. Changes have taken place in:
a) the techniques used in diving,
b) the rules and regulations governing diving,
c) the diver's objectives.

Diving techniques changed first. It is now illegal to use diving suits with compressed air tanks for oyster fishing, but the use of diving masks, snorkels, weighted belts and swim fins is perfectly legal, and these have greatly facilitated the diver's underwater maneuvers. Some divers also wear wet suits to protect them from the cold and allow them to remain longer in the water.

Beginning in 1970, new regulations set maximum quotas per lagoon and per diving season; a quota, for example, might be 40,000 oysters in three days. Therefore, the diver's aim no longer is to dive deep but rather to cover the maximum amount of ground in the shortest possible time.

Reserve stocks of oysters are being built up in each lagoon and it is illegal to harvest oysters less than 13 centimeters (4.5 inches) in diameter.

Furthermore, pearl diving isn't the great celebration it once was and fewer people are involved. Still, when the diving season opens at Takapoto, for instance, which has the best stocked lagoon, everybody and his brother heads for Takapoto. Speedboats piloted by brave navigators, often more or less reckless and unheeding of the perils of the sea, bring the divers from the nearby atolls of Takaroa, Manihi, Ahe, Aratika, and Arutua.

There is a reunion of the *fetii*, i.e. cousins, uncles, and in-laws that every Paumotu has in the neighboring islands. Then the diving begins, with each diver seeking out the *Pinctada margaritifera*, leaving behind the abundant but smaller *Pinctada maculata*.

The oysters are no longer opened and sacrificed in the instant search for pearls; they are jealously guarded instead for the production of cultured pearls. And "jealously guarded" is an accurate description since the minute a diver turns his head, his oysters are likely to disappear. The diver even has to sleep on the beach next to his catch to protect it from theft because each oyster of a size suitable for pearl culture (i.e., at least 13 centimeters in diameter or 5.25 inches) is worth 300 to 400 Pacific francs (about $2.00 to $2.50 U.S. at the rate of exchange when this book was published). A real oyster market then takes place, with the law of supply and demand in full sway. Owners and managers of pearl farms on neighboring islands don't stand much chance. First choice goes to the local cooperatives, second choice to local residents. Later, if there are any oysters left and anyone is still in the mood to sell, other buyers may have their innings (and they can consider themselves lucky if they aren't charged an extra — and illegal — tax in the bargain). Lucky for the pearl

Coral heads at water level. In their natural state, oysters attach themselves to the lower reaches of the coral.

1

*Underwater view (1) of coral colonies
of* acropora, porcillopora *and* porites.
(2) Madrepora *serve as a nursery to
small fish and (3) as a habitat for
various shellfish, such as the* bénitiers
*with their attractively colored lips and
also (5) pearl oysters.*

(4) Annelides polychetes *(Christmas
tree "worms"), a species of ringed
worm that retracts at the approach of
an intruder, are easily recognized by
their orange coloration.*

30

2

4

3

5

1

2

Among the madrepora porites *(1) notice, in the center of the photograph, a pearl oyster, half open to admit the sea water from which it strains its food. Around it are large* bénitiers *("baptismal font") mollusks on whose scalloped edges we can see a blue, green, or brown colored mantle. This mantle contains millions of single-celled algae who live in a symbiosis with the clam.*

Another pearl oyster (2) in the middle of a massive madreporic porcillopora *or "cauliflower coral."*

Below:

Manihi Lagoon in the Tuamotu Islands.

In the lower right hand corner, we see the pass, deep enough for boats to enter the lagoon. To the right of the pass, the village of Turipaoa, with 180 inhabitants referred to as Paumotu. On the outside of the atoll, the Pacific Ocean breaking against the coral reef which borders a strip of land planted with coconut trees. In the upper right corner, a "hoa," a natural channel between the lagoon and the ocean, usually very shallow, which allows the lagoon to be fed with sea water at high tide. Near this hoa, and to the left, the landing strip which can accommodate a medium-sized airplane (40 seats). At the same level, bordering the lagoon, the Kaina Village. Above the pass, at the tip of the main point, the grafting laboratory of the S.P.M. The light spots inside the lagoon are the tips of the "karena", coral columns rising abruptly from the bottom of the lagoon.

Facing page:

1 - Adult "pipi" (baby) oysters attached to a buoy. A Margaritifera has been placed among them to show the difference in size of these two Polynesian oysters.

2 - High coral mass, the top of a "Karena" which rises 90 to 100 feet from the bottom of the lagoon.

farms that diving is no longer the main source of oysters for pearl culture.

Collecting and raising spats

Young oysters have been collected since 1880 or even earlier, but collecting was not too popular when its chief purpose was to get oysters as a source of mother-of-pearl. In those days, after collecting the spats, one would have to wait seven or eight years to get a mother-of-pearl shell of good quality. And even then the shell didn't bring a very good price.

At the present time collecting is a "must" because diving alone can no longer supply the pearl farms. Furthermore, the market for spats has given a new impetus to collecting. A small oyster, three to six months old and measuring four centimeters in diameter (less than two inches), sells for 150 Pacific francs (1 dollar). A two year old, measuring 10-12 centimeters (5-6 inches), brings 300 to 400 Pacific francs.

Two conditions are required for collecting to take place:

• There must be a large enough stock of oysters to guarantee reproduction of the basic supply.

• Since the larvae do not attach themselves to the coral before three weeks, the currents in the lagoon must be gentle enough not to carry the larvae out to sea.

Both these conditions are met in closed lagoons such as Takapoto, where hundreds of thousand of spats are collected every year. The Japanese technicians prefer to graft young oysters for the production and quality of pearls.

Now, if diving for pearl oysters is not all that productive, why is it not eliminated entirely? The pearl farms could just as well replenish their stocks by means of collection. The reason that oyster diving continues seems to be: tradition. Although diving isn't the celebration it used to be, a diving season is occasionally authorized in part to keep the custom alive and in part to keep peace with the Paumotus. For instance in 1984 the natural oyster supply in Manihi lagoon was so poor that the government set an extremely low dive quota of 2000 oysters. The divers, always notorious for exceeding their quotas, brought in more than 10,000, ignoring the risk to the future of the oyster stocks in favor of short-term profits.

Collecting is most productive in closed lagoons. However, these are not usually the lagoons

most favorable for pearl production and the growth of mother-of-pearl. In open lagoons the tides bring in a richer supply of plankton to feed the oysters; for this reason oysters sometimes are moved from one lagoon to another. During such moves, care must be taken not to spread any diseases to which the oysters are subject.

Collecting the spats is really only a makeshift: a practical way of getting young oysters. It would be much more satisfying — and better for pearl culture — if the entire reproductive cycle of the *Pinctada margaritifera* could be controlled, with larvae and spats grown under quasi-laboratory conditions, but on an industrial scale. That's how the Japanese do it at the Ryou Kyou Pearl Company in Okinawa.

In Okinawa the oysters are placed in large tanks, where the females are "persuaded" by thermal shock (i.e., by changes in water temperature) to lay their eggs. The males fertilize them, and the fertilized eggs turn into larvae that are fed algae culture and raised artificially. Very few of the larvae (about 0.3 percent) develop into spats. This small percentage is adequate, however, because of the millions of eggs a female oyster lays at one time. A few years ago at the National Center for

Marine Exploitation (CNEXO) at Vairao, Tahiti, scientists performed experiments in an effort to get oysters to reproduce *in vitro* (i.e., in fiberglass tanks). Although the eggs were laid and fertilized in the usual manner and the larvae fed with the same algae culture, the larvae practically never developed into spats equipped with a foot and a shell.

Why these failures in a situation where the Japanese are relatively successful? First, because the conditions in Tahiti were more artificial than in Japan. All the experimenters from Tahiti who visited the Japanese hatcheries found them quite rudimentary, whereas in Tahiti the water was pumped from the depths of the sea instead of from a lagoon; it was also more carefully filtered, etc. Perhaps it was those very refinements effected in Tahiti that eliminated certain factors necessary to the growth of spats. We might compare the situation to the attempts made to provide an artificial diet for humans before the discovery of vitamins.

The oysters raised on Okinawa are also *Pinctada margaritifera*, but a smaller variety. CNEXO scientist Olivier Millous, who carried out the study, felt that the closed lagoons in French Polynesia may have caused the Polynesian oysters to be too inbred, with a consequent loss of genetic potential. Thus it might be desirable to cross-breed oysters from different lagoons — although we know there is always a risk involved when man interferes in an ecosystem.

I believe these experiments deserve another trial, under conditions that more closely resemble those found in nature. They might be conducted in the Tuamotus, for instance, since that seems to be the oysters' favorite place, and the experimenters might well keep in mind the importance of the coral heads where oysters normally live.

Until such time as this research succeeds, as we know it will some day, we shall have to go on collecting spats to stock the pearl farms. These farms, full of oysters that in one or two years will become adults ready to reproduce, can develop into breeding centers that in turn will lend themselves to collecting, provided the tides in their local lagoons are not too strong.

The increase in the price of young oysters, brought about because of the strong demand for them, has led to the establishment of collecting stations. Such stations will continue to be built until prices either stabilize or come down, when the supply of spats exceeds the demand. Pearl diving and the folklore that surrounds it are almost out of date. I would even say they ought to become so, at least until such time as larvae from the pearl farms have succeeded in replenishing the natural oyster beds. On the whole I think we can look forward to the future with confidence. Pessimists will say that man's greed was what caused the oyster beds, once so abundant, to be exploited almost to extinction. But financial motives, as well as the rarity of the oysters, have slowed that exploitation. At present it is the profit motive that has stimulated the growth of pearl farming and led to the replenishment of the lagoons. Today the great risk in certain lagoons is over-population, which might cause ecological changes leading to epidemics among the oysters or a drop in pearl production. Thus far these developments haven't taken place, but a farsighted government should think about limiting the proliferation of pearl farms in some of the lagoons that are easiest to access from the main island, Tahiti.

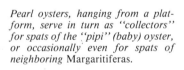

Pearl oysters, hanging from a platform, serve in turn as "collectors" for spats of the "pipi" (baby) oyster, or occasionally even for spats of neighboring Margaritiferas.

The pearl oyster of Polynesia

There are more than 70 species of oysters that can produce pearls, not to mention other kinds of pearl-bearing shellfish such as the *haliotis, pinna, tridacna* (called "benitier" in French because it has been used as a baptismal font), *strombus, unionidae,* saltwater and freshwater mussels.

Most pearl oysters belong to the *Pinctada* family which is a different species from the edible oysters of the *Ostreidae* family.

Pearl oysters are divided into two large groups:

• First, those which have thin shells that are of no commercial value, and therefore are prized only for their pearls.

These include: *Pinctada martensi fucata,* found in China and Japan.

Pinctada radiata, found in the Persian Gulf.
Pinctada vulgaris, found in India and Sri Lanka.
Pinctada fucata, found in Australia and Papua New Guinea.
Pinctada maculata, the so called *"pipi"* (or baby) oyster found in Polynesia.

• Second, there are the large oysters which are prized both for their mother-of-pearl shells and the large pearls they produce:

Pinctada maxima, found in the Philippines, Papua New Guinea, Australia, Indonesia, and Burma.

This species, called the silver-lipped or gold-lipped oyster, produces the large white or golden pearls known as "South Seas pearls."

Left:
Golden-lipped Pinctada maxima.

Right:
Black-lipped Pinctada margaritifera.

Pinctada margaritifera, found chiefly in Polynesia but also in the Red Sea, Micronesia, Indonesia, Mexico, Panama, Peru and even in Japan (Okinawa).

This is the black-lipped oyster that produces black pearls.

There are several varieties of *Pinctada margaritifera*, of which the largest is the one found in Polynesia, named *Pinctada margaritifera Cumingi* for Professor Cumings, who first described it.

Although the black-lipped oyster has an extensive habitat, the only countries at present where black pearls are cultivated and sold are Japan (Okinawa) and French Polynesia.

There is another magnificent variety of oysters known as the "black-winged oyster" (*pteria penguin*) which so far has yielded only half-pearls, called "*mabe*", from the name of the oyster that produces it.

Pinctada margaritifera Cumingi

This bivalve mollusk, belonging to the *Pteriidae* family, has two symmetrical shells hinged by a ligament. So powerful is the adductor muscle that connects and holds the two shells that it creates an indentation on the inner surface of the shells themselves at the point where it is inserted. *Pinctada margaritifera* is characterized by the greenish-black color of the mother-of-pearl on the edges of the shell's inner surface.

In the adult stage this oyster attains a diameter of 15-20 centimeters (6-8 inches). It can live as long as 30 years, and may reach 30 centimeters (12 inches) in diameter and weigh up to five kilos (11 lbs).

Each half of the shell is lined with a mantle that corresponds to the fine membrane which covers the interior of the shell of edible oysters and contracts when it is touched.

1 - Interior of the Pinctada margaritifera *shell.*

2 - Exterior of the Pinctada margaritifera *shell.*

3/4 - Pinctada maculata, *the "pipi" (baby) oysters.*

1

2

3

4

Pinctada margaritifera *in all its splendor. Its mother-of-pearl lining consists of aragonite crystals that grow lighter in color from the outer edges toward the center. The area where the adductor muscle was attached is clearly visible.*

Formation of the shell

It is the mantle which secretes the shell, with each part of the mantle specializing in secreting a different layer. At its edges the mantle forms a roll or lobe, the outer part of which produces the *periostracum* or outer layer of the shell. That outer layer is made of a horny organic substance called *conchioline* which is laid down in overlapping layers — similar, if you will, to the layered feathers on a bird. The external wall of the mantle lobe secretes the rainbow-colored middle layer of the shell, consisting of *calcite* crystals in a conchioline matrix. The total external surface of the mantle within the lobe secretes crystals of calcium carbonate called *aragonite*, which is deposited in layers on a delicate web of protein matter (conchioline) and forms the inner layer of the shell. The inner layer is what we call mother-of-pearl, the edges of which have the coloration (greenish-black with purple highlights)

characteristic of the *Pinctada margaritifera* and also of the so-called "black" pearls of Polynesia.

Since the periphery of the mantle secretes a tinted mother-of-pearl and the center produces a white nacre, it is clear that if we want to produce black pearls it is the edge of the mantle that must be grafted. The central portion would be more likely to produce white pearls. The external face of the mantle (the part touching the shell) is lined with an epithelial layer made up of cells comparable to those that form the human skin and glands, such as the sebaceous and sweat glands, that are indentations of the skin. In the oyster these epithelial cells are responsible for secreting the organic matter and calcium carbonate that make up the shell. It is useful to know how the shell is produced, i.e. by a process quite similar to the growth of our fingernails, because it is this same process that produces pearls.

Different stages in polishing the outside of a Margaritifera *shell: (1) Natural state. (2 & 3) polishing gradually removes the* periostracum *layer, revealing (4) the prismatic layer composed of calcite crystals.*

1

2

3

4

ANATOMY OF THE OYSTER

The mantle has two sides surrounding the palleal cavity which contains the body and the various organs of the oyster. When we examine an oyster, it is astonishing to find that this humble creature has almost the same organs as a human being. (On one occasion when the nurses on my staff were helping me to dissect an ordinary edible oyster, they were so surprised by the sight of the creature's beating heart that for at least six months they couldn't bear to eat oysters.) Indeed, like all the rest of us, the *Pinctada margaritifera* has:

• A respiratory apparatus consisting of gills.

• A cardio-vascular system consisting of a heart with two auricles, one ventricle, and blood vessels.

• A digestive apparatus consisting of a mouth equipped with four labial palps or feelers, a stomach, a digestive tube with attached liver and pancreas, and an anus. This digestive system allows the oyster to feed on plankton, microscopic algae, zooplankton, organic matter and minerals dissolved in sea water, and even on its own eggs and larvae.

• A nervous system, admittedly rather rudimentary, consisting of three pairs of interconnected ganglia.

• A means of locomotion consisting of a foot equipped with lifting and retracting muscles. (The foot is really functional only during the period when the oyster is attaching itself to some kind of support.) The foot also contains a gland which secretes the byssus, the filaments that allow the oyster to attach. The secretion is very efficient; an oyster that is detached from its support and moved will reattach itself elsewhere in a matter of days.

• Genitals. A *Pinctada margaritifera* can successively (but not simultaneously) be either male or female, depending on external conditions. Sexual maturity is reached between two and three years, with males predominating among young oysters. Later the number of females increases, but if the oysters are subject to stress or poor nutrition, the percentage of males again increases. The gonad or sex gland (male or female, as the case may be) is a rather large mass that completely covers all the internal organs. In appearance it is a downward projecting whitish sack that is clearly visible when the oyster is sexually inactive. It is into this sack that the nucleus and a piece of mantle are inserted in order to produce a cultured pearl. During periods when the oyster is sexually fertile (and these periods occur several times a year, with maximum fertility in April and October) the sex gland increases in size and looks different in the two sexes, becoming granular and orange-colored in the female, smooth and yellow in the male. During periods of maturation the male oyster develops spermatozoa and the female develops ovules.

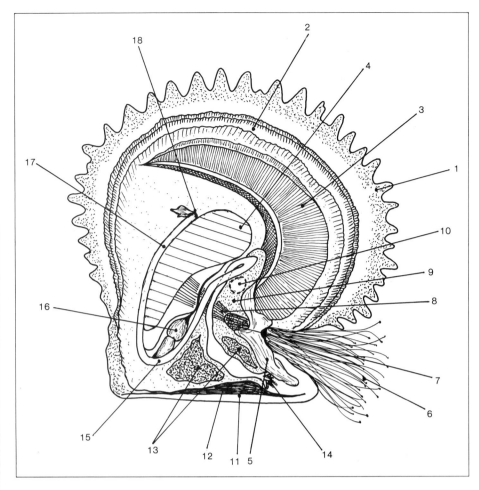

SCHEMATIC DIAGRAM
OF PINCTADA MARGARITIFERA
(right valve)

Taken from a drawing furnished by EVAAM (Department of Fisheries,) Tahiti.

1 - Valve with unnacred edge
2 - Mantle
3 - Gills
4 - Adductor muscle
5 - Foot
6 - Byssus filaments
7 - Byssus-generating gland
8 - Foot retractor muscle
9 - Gonad or reproductive gland
10 - Point where nucleus is inserted
11 - Hinge
12 - Ligament
13 - Hepato-pancreas
14 - Mouth surrounded by labial palpes
15 - Digestive tube
16 - Heart
17 - Rectum
18 - Anus

Photographs of two Margaritifera *showing anatomy.*

Tufts of miki-miki *ready to be made into collectors (also see facing page).*

Reproduction

Since an oyster is held in place by its byssus, oysters do not copulate. Their sexual products are ejected right into the sea water, where the eggs are fertilized by the spermatozoa. Sexual emission by one oyster triggers the other oysters to follow suit. The enormous number of sperm and eggs deposited (up to 40 million eggs by an adult female!) increases the chance the two will meet. Nevertheless, because of the way the sexual materials are deposited, breeding will occur only if many oysters are concentrated in a fairly limited space. This is why Professor Gilbert Ranson has been saying since 1957 that the best idea would be to set up "reproduction parks" in each lagoon. After an egg has been fertilized, it divides rapidly and becomes a D-shaped larva equipped with a kind of movable sail that lets it swim close to the surface, where it is carried along by the currents. It remains in this larval, planktonic stage between 24 and 31 days, by which time it measures 300 microns, has grown the foot which allows it to attach itself to a support, and has developed an embryonic shell that gives it weight and pulls it toward the bottom. The larva then attaches itself to some kind of support and grows into a spat. Larvae will attach to almost anything: the sea floor, a coral head, a bigger oyster, or a collector basket especially prepared for that purpose.

During their planktonic stage the larvae are devoured by many species of zooplankton (planktonic animals) and every kind of fish,

Pinctadae margaritiferae *in various stages of growth.*

but it is especially when they attach that they are decimated by being choked in the sand or consumed by the live coral. The spats that survive will grow and develop into adults in two or three years, provided they don't fall victim to their other natural enemies. That is the normal course of events in nature. Man, however, intervenes in their life cycle by setting out collectors to which some of the spats attach themselves as their support. As soon as they do that, the young oysters move into an artificial cycle in which they are constantly observed and protected. They are "brought up" or cultivated, and because of man's protection a much larger percentage survive.

Collecting spats

In order to be successful, collecting must take place where there is a concentration of adult oysters, either in nature or in a pearl farm where the oysters are kept together by design. The currents must be gentle enough not to carry all the floating larvae toward the pass through the reef. For that reason, collecting is most profitable in closed lagoons (i.e., lagoons that do not have a pass) such as Takapoto.

GROWTH RATE OF THE PINCTADA MARGARITIFERA	
Age	**Size**
1 month	250-300 microns
2 months	2-3 millimeters
3 months	1-2 cm. (3/4 inch)
6 months	4-5 cm. (2 inches)
1 year	7-8 cm. (3 inches)
2 years	10-12 cm. (4-5 inches)
3 years	12-15 cm. (6 inches)

Collecting stations

Basically a collecting station is an arrangement of ropes about 100 meters (300 feet) long on which collector baskets are hung. The ropes are suspended from buoys and anchored at the bottom by heavy weights.

Collectors

The collectors should be placed between one and two meters (3 to 6 feet) below the surface of the water. They must be made of non-decaying material, with many nooks and crannies where the spats can attach themselves out of the reach of fish and other predators.

Various natural products are used to make the collectors: the *uu* and *miki miki* (*Pemphis acidula*) bushes that grow on coral atolls, fiber from the bark of the coconut palm, and the fiber on the outside of the coconuts themselves. Synthetic materials can also be used, such as awning material or foam rubber remnants from the manufacture of the thong sandals ("go-aheads") so popular in Polynesia. Generally these materials are enclosed in either plastic or wire netting to protect the spats from predators.

Wrapped in a net, the collector makes a small cylindrical package about 60 centimeters long and 20-30 cm. in diameter (2 feet × 8-12 inches) which is hung from the ropes of the collecting station. The collectors are placed in the station in December and brought back up six months later, then returned to the water for another six months.

Harvesting and handling the spats

When the collectors are hauled up after six months, one sees the little shells attached to various parts of the collector inside the protective netting. The shells, measuring 1 to 4 centimeters (.5 to 1.5 inches), will not all be shells of *Pinctada margaritifera*.

Over 80 percent will be *Pinctada maculata*, the "*pipi*" oyster, together with other shellfish which must be separated from the young mother-of-pearl oysters. The latter are detached from their support, not by pulling them loose but by carefully cutting the byssus.

Next the youngsters are sorted according to size and placed in baskets and containers covered with wire netting of a mesh fine enough to prevent the spats from falling through. Every two or three months as they grow, the spats (which attach to each other as well as to the basket) are separated, cleaned and measured, then sorted again in smaller groups and placed in baskets with a coarser mesh.

The baskets are hung from a growing platform submerged at a depth of 5 to 8 meters (16 to 25 feet).

Piercing the shell

When the spats reach a diameter of 6 to 8 centimeters (2.5 to 3 inches), they undergo their first operation: shell piercing.

The youngsters are brought out of the lagoon and placed temporarily in a tank filled with sea water.

An electric drill equipped with a delicate bit is used to drill two holes in the heel of the shell, near the hinge. There is no danger of wounding the little oyster because these holes are actually on the outside of the hinge itself. A nylon thread is strung through the two holes and tied in a loop, which then serves to attach the oyster, heel upward, to the ropes in the raising station.

From this time forward the oyster will live its life on the ropes, so to speak, hanging heel upward.

This is the opposite of its natural position but the oyster doesn't seem to mind. A chain of 10 or 20 oysters is formed and hung on a growing platform. The same platform will be used later on after the oyster is grafted and implanted with a nucleus.

Clockwise:

1 - Collecting station for spats, with buoys and markers stretching about 100 yards across a lagoon.

2 - Interior of a collector made of scraps from the manufacture of thong sandals.

3 - Collector ready for submersion. It consists of a soft rubber center wrapped in awning material and a protective wire cage.

4 - Capture station raised out of the water to show the collectors hanging from a cable.

5 - Collector opened to show the young pearl and "pipi" oysters that are attached.

1 - Pearl oyster shell with its nylon string for suspension.

2 - Exterior and interior of a young pearl oyster shell that was perforated by a predator.

3 - An old oyster that has been attacked by a "baliste" fish (L. sufflamen bursa) in an area already weakened by cliona and lithophagus parasites.

Facing page:

1 - Platform made of metal pipes from which are suspended strings of pearl oysters, before or after grafting.
2 - Tripods and metal fencing used at the Société Perlière de Manihi for suspension of pearl oysters.

2

3

The platforms

There are several kinds of platform, the most common being a fixed structure made of galvanized metal pipes, with the main supporting pipes standing on the bottom. Floating platforms, held at the required depth by heavy weights, may also be used. The S.P.M. (Société Perliere de Manihi) uses long metal grills supported by tripods.

Although the oysters can simply hang on a rope tied to the crosspieces of the platform, whenever there are predatory fish such as the Baliste (called *oiri* in Tahitian) or the parrotfish, it is preferable to tie their nylon loops to the inside of a protective wire mesh cylinder. The cylinder, completely closed, is then attached to the platform.

The oysters should hang about 10 meters (30 feet) under water so that they are sheltered from turbulence on the surface of the lagoon, particularly during hurricane season. They must also stand 3 to 5 meters (10 to 16 feet) from the sandy bottom because sand is another of the oyster's enemies.

Once the oysters are hung from a platform, it is a matter of waiting for them to grow and reach a stage where they are ready for grafting. Nonetheless there must be regular inspections of the cylinders and their attachments, the ropes and the chains of oysters. Above all it is important to check for predators and any damage they may have done. If the predators are sedentary, such as tetrodons (blowfish) or octopus, they must be eliminated or wire mesh cylinders should be used to protect the oysters as described above. Spats are not always raised in the lagoon where they will be used for the production of pearls. Most of the oysters grafted at Manihi, for instance, originate at Takapoto. When oysters are to be moved, it is best to move them when they are young, 4 to 6 centimeters (1.75 to 2.25 inches) in length. They weigh less and are easily transported in small tanks filled with sea water, which can be changed at intervals. The mortality rate in such moves is low, even if a boat trip of eight to twelve hours, including loading and unloading, is involved. Taking adult oysters out of the water and simply transporting them by boat results in a higher mortality, but in any case, losses usually do not exceed 10 percent. Air transport is faster, of course, and also less traumatic but is more expensive.

As soon as the traveling oysters reach their destination, they are put into a "park" in shallow water where they will stay for a few days before they are attached to a platform. After that at least three months of recuperation and acclimatization must be allowed before they can be grafted.

Because of all these trials, only a few of the tens of millions of eggs and spermatozoa that were originally ejected into the sea survive to reach maturity.

Under the quasi-laboratory conditions of reproduction and feeding larvae with algae cultures, as is done at the Ryou Kyou Pearl Company in Okinawa, the success rate is still less that one in a thousand. And even with the methods described above, in which the spats are protected by baskets, only half of the young oysters collected live to be adults.

Predators alone are not responsible for this high mortality rate; parasites also take their toll. Perforating sponges (*cliona*) and boring bivalves (*lithophagus*), for example, weaken the shell and make the oyster less resistant to predators. There is also an oyster "sickness" found chiefly at Hikueru and in the Gambier Islands, an infection that causes the mantle to be retracted and deformed, which in turn results in a malformation of the mother-of-pearl layers inside the shell. In this area this sickness is known to be fatal to half of the oysters that are grafted. This sickness recently made its appearence in many atolls of the Tuamotus around Takapoto and Manihi and will certainly limit the production of black pearls in the future.

1

2

The pearls of Polynesia

Long ago — and even in more recent times — the basic reason for oyster diving was to obtain mother-of-pearl. Mother-of-pearl was exported and used to manufacture buttons and decorate furniture, or used locally in hand-crafted articles and jewelry. Discovering a valuable pearl, which happened less and less often as the older oysters disappeared, was a windfall that lent spice and glamour to the otherwise difficult and boring job of diving for mother-of-pearl.

It has been estimated that by 1960 divers were lucky if they found one sizeable pearl per 100,000 shells opened. During the 1969-1970 diving season at Takapoto, not one valuable pearl was found in 300,000 oysters brought up. Finding a really good pearl was something like winning the lottery, and that gave it a certain appeal for the Tahitians, who are gamblers at heart. One has only to observe the popularity of the numerous lotteries taking place in Papeete every week (not to mention the clandestine gambling dens) to be convinced of that.

Natural pearls

The pearl produced by the *Pinctada margaritifera*, the most common oyster in Polynesia, usually is a "black" pearl (called in Tahitian *poe rava*: greenish-black or peacock). Such pearls can have highlights of red, purple, copper, gray, silver or steel blue. In fact, such a pearl can take on all the colors that show on the edge of the black-lipped oyster's shell. The shape of the pearl is often baroque (i.e., irregular), but may be pear-shaped or perfectly round. Its size varies with the age of the oyster and the amount of time the pearl has been developing. If we go by the growth rate of cultured pearls (3 microns per day), we can say it takes about five years to grow a pearl 10 millimeters in diameter (about 3/8 of an inch). How are these fine natural pearls formed? The classic explanation is that a grain of sand, a parasite or other foreign body penetrates the

oyster and causes an irritation. Then, in self-defense supposedly, the oyster secretes nacre to isolate the intruder.

This theory doesn't hold water. Assuming that a foreign body (usually a parasite) did invade the oyster, it would have to carry epithelial cells with it because we know that it is epithelial cells that secrete the nacre that eventually forms a pearl. This explains why natural pearls are almost always found in the inside part of the mantle, whereas cultured pearls are artificially grafted into the gonad where there is more room to place the nucleus. Because they are so rare, such natural black pearls are highly prized, although they are not different in their structure or appearance from cultured pearls which have exactly the same characteristics and are just as brilliant. Only an x-ray showing a nucleus can distinguish between the two. The inflated price of natural pearls is beginning to come down, and as in the case of fine white pearls, the fact that they are natural soon will add little to their value.

Natural baroque pearl (actual size).

Cultured pearls

With the introduction of cultured pearls, we moved away from the "lottery" of natural pearls and into an era of scientifically organized production. We have already talked about the way Mikimoto, between 1893 and 1907, perfected the technique of growing cultured pearls, how the Tahiti Department of Fisheries in 1963 pioneered the first attempts to grow cultured pearls in Polynesia, and how those early efforts inspired the Rosenthal brothers to establish the first pearl farm in 1968.

Now let's look at the different stages in the production of cultured pearls.

The Theory of Pearl Culture

In order to grow a cultured pearl, a tiny ball, which acts as the seed or nucleus of the pearl, must be inserted in the body of the oyster.

At the same time, a fragment of epithelium must be placed in contact with the nucleus. The epithelium spreads around the nucleus and forms a "pearl sack." The pearl sack then is made of epithelial tissue which will secrete nacre, depositing it in concentric layers around the nucleus to produce a pearl.

Pearl culture thus requires:

— A pearl oyster.
— A nucleus.
— A graft of epithelium from the mantle of an oyster.
— A surgical operation. Like any operation, this calls for an operating room, commonly called a "laboratory" or, more modestly, a "grafting shack."

1. The Pearl Oyster — For a *Pinctada margaritifera* to be considered for operating, it must be 10 to 12 centimeters (4 to 5 inches) in diameter. The oyster is obtained either by diving or by cultivation in a pearl farm. At present Japanese technicians prefer the products of the oyster farms because they tend to be younger and healthier.

In any case, whether the oyster has been fished (i.e. dived for) or raised at the farm, a hole must be drilled in the hinge and three months given to become accustomed to the platform where it will live permanently. Before being grafted, an oyster must be in perfect physical condition. Depending on the location of the platforms and whether conditions are more or less favorable, the grafting technicians usually find a percentage of oysters on which they will refuse to operate because the tissues are not healthy enough. These oysters

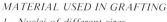

MATERIAL USED IN GRAFTING

1 - Nuclei of different sizes.

2 - Grafting instruments. From left to right:
Two spreaders for opening the oyster shell.
Spatulas for separating tissue.
Instruments with scalpel at one end and graft-carrier at the other.
Nucleus-carrier.
Dilator used to enlarge the cavity into which nucleus and graft are to be inserted.
Scissors for cutting off the byssus.
Tweezers.
Slicer and scissors used for preparing grafts.

are returned to the water to await a more favorable time.

We are not talking here about sickness but rather of a general state of health which likely will improve in a different location where there is a richer supply of plankton.

If the gonads are swollen with sexual material, this may also be a reason to postpone the operation for a few days, giving the oyster time to deposit its eggs or sperm.

In case of sickness, the oysters are sacrificed because they wouldn't be able to survive the grafting operation.

2. The Nucleus — After trying glass and lead pellets, pearl specialists determined that they had a better success rate with tiny balls made of shell.

The nuclei customarily used today, then, are made of the shells of fresh water mussels, e.g. the "pig toe" and "washboard" mussels, which come from the Mississipi River. The shells are cut into cubes, then ground with stone disks until they are perfectly round, polished, pearl-colored pellets 6 to 8 millimeters (about 1/4 inch) in diameter. It is important for the nucleus to be of almost the same density and resistance as the pearl substance so that it doesn't fracture when the pearl is pierced. Because these mussels are getting scarce, pearl farmers have tried to make a satisfactory artificial nucleus using synthetic resins, but so far their efforts have been unsuccessful.

There must be different sizes of nuclei so that a technician can select a nucleus corresponding to the size of the oyster and its gonad sack. In some cases, called "supergrafts," the nucleus can be as large as 10 millimeters.

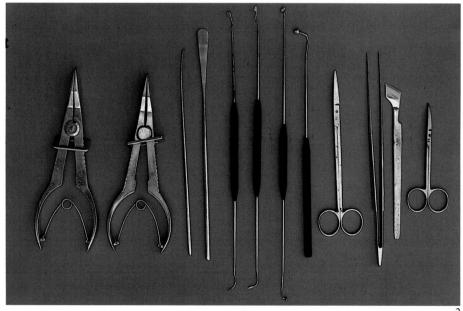

1

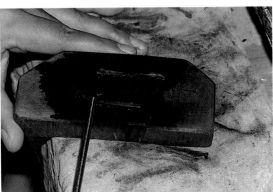

2

3

4

5

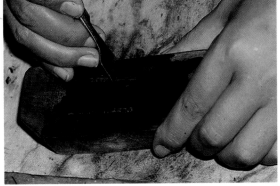

6

3. The Graft — Grafting is absolutely indispensable to the production of a cultured pearl.

The nucleus can even be omitted and a pearl produced by means of the epithelial graft alone; such pearls are called "keshis." But a nucleus alone will produce nothing. Half-pearls, grown against the shell, are not grafted, but those are not the true pearls created inside the body of the oyster.

To understand what happens when a graft is made, let's review briefly the biology of grafting.

The graft consists of removing a fragment of tissue which is then transplanted into another place of the body where it will survive and proliferate.

If the tissue comes from the same individual onto which it is grafted, it is called an *autograft*. To take the example of a burn case: if the skin grafted on a patient's face comes from his own thigh, it is an autograft. In human beings the body accepts an autograft as a permanent addition; the oyster accepts such grafts in exactly the same way. In pearl production, however, autografts are not the usual procedure.

What normally is done is to take the tissue from another individual of the same species; this is called a *homograft*. Kidney transplant is an example of a homograft in humans, and we know that in some cases the receiving organism has a defensive (immune) reaction that causes the transplant to be rejected. That defensive mechanism can be controlled by ensuring compatibility between the tissues of donor and donee, with best results obtained between parent and child or between siblings. Alternatively medication can be given to lessen the patient's immune reaction.

Such defensive reactions do not seem to exist

in the oyster. Therefore, the normal grafting procedure is by means of homograft. One oyster is sacrificed, yielding enough grafting tissue to start the pearl-producing process in about 60 of its fellows. I mentioned earlier that oysters growing in the same lagoon show a close genetic relationship; this may be one of the reasons why a homograft in oysters normally "takes" successfully.

There is still a third method of grafting in which the graft is made from one species to another, as was done in the case of Baby Fay, whose heart was replaced with the heart of a baboon. This is called a *heterograft* or *xenograft* (from the Greek *xeno*, meaning foreign). In spite of immuno-suppressants, such grafts have very little chance of success in humans.

It would be interesting in the case of oysters to study the chances of grafting between different but closely related species. Would it be possible, for instance, to produce black pearls in the large "benetier" shellfish by grafting them with a piece of *Pinctada margaritifera*? The "benitier" can measure up to 60 centimeters (24 inches) across and they are smaller but numerous in some of the Polynesian atolls. Well, it's an idea...

But to return to practical matters, here is how the graft is prepared. The technician selects a young, medium-sized oyster whose peripheral shell is a beautiful green-black color with red highlights. Color is important because it is the graft from the donor oyster, not the donee, that secretes the nacre to form a pearl. The donor oyster is then sacrificed; the mantle is removed from both sides of its shell and set aside for grafting. The lobe is not used. The technician stretches the mantle on a wooden board, taking care to observe which is the external side (the side growing next to the shell) because it is the epithelium on that side that secretes the nacre. With a scalpel he makes a series of cuts in the mantle 3 millimeters apart, first lengthwise, then crosswise, so that he has several rows of tiny squares measuring 3 millimeters on each side. Each of these squares will be a graft, the outer side of which must be placed against the nucleus in the gonad of the receiving oyster. The grafts must be kept wet throughout these operations. We now have the three elements needed to make pearls:

• Nuclei which will form the seeds of the pearls and will be inserted in the gonad of the receiving oyster.

Upper left:
Laboratory of the S.P.M., Manihi atoll in the Tuamotu Archipelago.

Below:
Panoramic view of Manihi lagoon. From left to right: the Laboratory of the S.P.M., airport buildings, and at right the Kaina Village Hotel.

Facing page, above:
Laboratory of Tahiti Pacific Pearl Co. at Moe-Moe, Manihi lagoon.

SADAO ISHIBASHI

Sadao Ishibashi was born in 1950 in Tokyo. After high school, he entered the University of Tokai. where he studied Marine Biology for five years (which corresponds to the level of our Master's degree). After University, Ishibashi, then aged 23, started working with "Columbia Import-Export" in the field of scientific equipment. After faithfully working in this firm for three years, Ishibashi wished to visit other countries and he was hired by a pearl farm in Broome, West Australia. There, he learned and gained practical experience in pearl grafting. One year later, searching for new techniques and other varieties of oysters, he moved to Indonesia and met his true master in the art of pearl grafting, Itaru Nishimura. He stayed two years in Indonesia and then spent six months in Thailand where he found there were not enough oysters to be grafted, so he went back to Indonesia.

He visited Polynesia for the first time in 1978 and worked at the "S.P.M." in Manihi. He was able to enjoy the rare quality of pearls and the political stability of French Polynesia. However he encountered some difficulty with the managers of the firm. He returned to Indonesia for two years and came back to Tahiti in 1981 in order to work with "Tahiti Pacific Pearls", "Tuamotu Perles" and "Royal Tahitian Pearl". Year after year, he perfected his technique.

Contrary to most Japanese grafting technicians, Sadao speaks English and Tahitian fluently; he also knows French quite well which makes communication much easier and creative. Sadao spends 10 months out of twelve in French Polynesia. He is one of the most successful technicians in regards to Tahitian pearls.

1 - The grafting table.
2 - Oysters to be grafted, their shells held open by a wooden wedge.
3 - Orientable oyster holder.
4 - Grafting technician preparing to insert a nucleus.

Facing page:
1 - Grafting a pearl oyster: Sadao Ishibashi in action.
2 - Closeup of insertion of the nucleus. Notice how the technician holds his instruments, with a touch as delicate as a surgeon's.

• Squares of nacre-secreting epithelial tissue, which will be positioned against the nucleus in the same incision.
• The healthy young pearl oysters to be grafted. We are ready now to watch the grafting operation, so let's take a look at the operating room.

4. The Laboratory or "Grafting Shack" - Although it may be a more elaborate structure, the laboratory usually is housed in a shack built on the coral reef next to the deep water where the platforms stand. Thus the lab is close to the oysters and no extra steps are required. A deck built of boards slightly separated from one another allows the oysters to be hung back in the water as soon as the operation is finished. Next to the deck is a small covered terrace; this is a holding area for tanks that contain oysters awaiting surgery.

The operating room itself will be larger or smaller depending on the size of the pearl farm and the number of grafting technicians on the staff. Each technician requires just a small space (one to two square meters or between 9 and 18 square feet) equipped with a table for his instruments, a stock of nuclei, grafts prepared as described above, and natural light provided by an opening behind him. Some technicians like a cubicle that encloses the table on three sides and shields them from side lighting and also from curious glances. There must also be enough room for other employees to fill the box on the technician's left with open oysters and take away the grafted oysters on his right, returning them to hang in the water. Some labs are built on floating platforms, like big catamarans, that can be moved around at will, but these can only be used in lagoons in which the waters are perfectly calm because the grafting operation calls for complete stability and steadiness.

Now, if the Japanese technician is not too jealous of the secrets of his technique, we will look over his shoulder and watch him operate.

The Grafting Operation

The divers will have brought the oysters to the surface and carried them to the grafting shack. There they are removed from their protective netting or detached from their rope, and the nylon loop holding the shell is cut. The oysters are then cleaned and scraped to remove growths and parasites, and then they are placed in a tank half full of sea water to

1

2

3

4

1

2

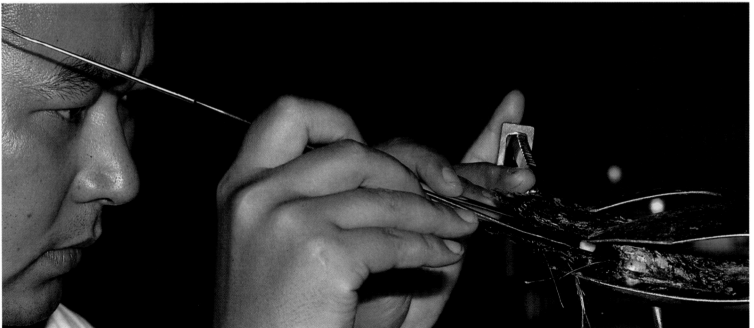

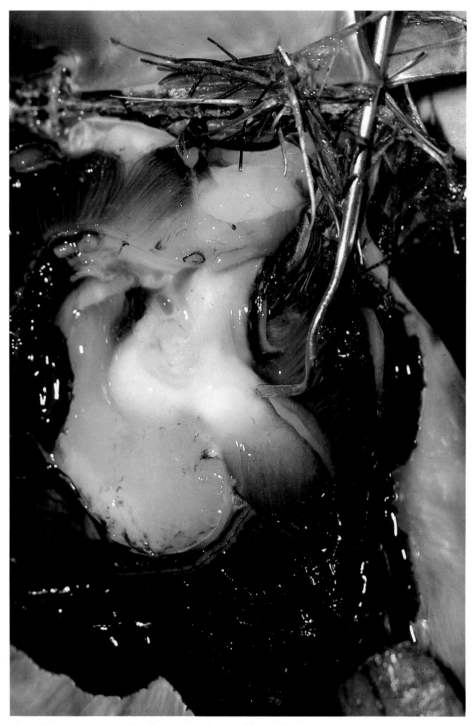

The nucleus has been positioned correctly in the gonad (sex gland.) The tip of the instrument points to the location of the nucleus.

Above, the brown liquid is blood oozing from the incision.

a spring that holds the oyster in the correct position in front of the operator. Using a similar dilator, he separates the shells enough to see inside. So that the adductor muscle won't be injured, the opening must not exceed 1 centimeter (3/8 inch), and this makes the operation more difficult. With the oyster thus partially open and exposed, the operator uses a special spatula to move the mantle and gills toward the upper and lower halves of the shell, allowing him to see the internal organs. He locates the foot and byssus, which he cuts. He then finds the gonad (sex gland), which will be more or less developed and recognizable by its yellow color and its downward extension that is more shiny. It is in this extension of the gonad that the technician must create a tiny cavity in which he will place the nucleus and epithelial graft.

The incision is not made directly into the sack but a little bit higher and from back to front, away from the hinge. Using a special instrument, the operator inserts the graft into the cavity, with the exterior, nacre-secreting side facing up. Then by means of another special instrument, he places the nucleus on top of the graft.

Finally, with the spatula he puts the organs back in place, closes the oyster, and puts it in another tank with the hinge toward the top so that gravity doesn't pull the nucleus toward the incision. With this, the operation is over. It has taken one to two minutes.

End of operation

Make no mistake: grafting is real surgery. It requires manual skill, good judgment and knowledge of oyster anatomy. The technician works on friable tissues, using instruments inserted in a narrow opening, and he has only a minimum amount of time.

After the operation, an assistant feeds a new nylon loop through the holes in the shell and adds the oyster, still hinge upward, to a chain of 10 of its fellows. Once the chain is formed, it is hung from the deck next to the lab and waits there to be picked up by a diver and returned to an underwater platform.

Does the technician operate on every oyster that comes to him? Not at all. Some candidates have to be postponed or definitely rejected because they are:

• Too old. These will be used to produce keshis or half-pearls.

wait grafting. Next an assistant removes an oyster from the tank and opens its shell with a special instrument that is inserted between the valves of the shell in a closed position, then opened gradually. Ratchets in the instrument prevent the shell from closing. When the shell is open about one centimeter (3/8 inch), a small wooden wedge is inserted to hold it open and the dilator is removed.

The oysters then are aligned vertically, open end upward, in a box to the technician's left. The technician takes an oyster and sets it on a "shell holder" — a pedestal equipped with two spoons. The upper spoon is mounted on

• Too young. If the gonad is not sufficiently developed, the oyster is returned to the water to be grafted at a later date.
• Not healthy enough. These will be returned to the water and to a better environment, if possible.
• Definitely sick, in which case they will be sacrificed.

Post operative care

The trauma of the operation leaves the oysters in a weakened condition and for a certain period of time they must be specially protected against predators. Either they are placed temporarily in a *nursery* — a fenced park — or they may be returned permanently to their platform, protected by wire mesh or netting.

Mortality

Some oysters (up to 10 percent or more) cannot withstand the operation. They die for different reasons:
• Too much time out of the lagoon (more than 10 or 12 hours).
• Exposure to the sun.
• Injury to the adductor muscle from being forced open.
• Bleeding during the operation. Oysters do have a fluid analogous to blood (although it is a lighter brown) and they may lose about a third of that circulatory fluid as a result of grafting.

Rejection of the nucleus

Sometimes the nucleus is quickly rejected after the operation, either because of a faulty perforation of the gonad or because too big a nucleus was used relative to the size of the oyster and its gonad. Sometimes the nucleus or even the pearl itself is rejected later on. When the nucleus alone is rejected and the graft remains in place, the result will be a keshi. If both nucleus and graft are rejected, the oyster will heal; a second graft can be attempted later.

The usual way to find out whether the nucleus has been refused is by fluoroscopy. By this means a technician can see whether or not there is a pearl in the oyster.

Formation of a pearl

A successful operation is followed by a waiting period that lasts an average of two years. During that time the pearl begins to grow, then becomes bigger and more beautiful.

In the first two or three weeks, the *pearl sack* forms. The graft which was placed underneath the nucleus is partially absorbed,

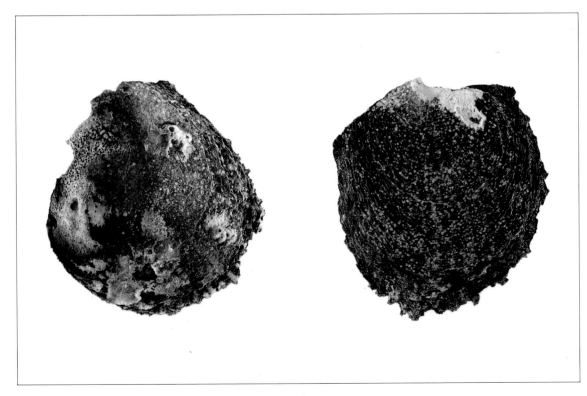

Shells of two old oysters, showing deterioration of the valves due to attack by various parasites.

1 - Tahiti Pacific Pearl Co. *pearl farm, seen from the lagoon.*

2 - The pearl farm gives its guests all the benefits of modern technology. Solar energy is used successfully to produce electricity for the laboratory and for staff housing. It is a pleasant surprise to find conveniences such as electric lighting, a deep freezer and refrigerator, a generator to produce hot water, and video equipment. The grafting technicians and other personnel have private bungalows.

3 - Pearl oysters are hung from a deck like the one shown here while awaiting grafting and again while awaiting their trip back to the platform where they will remain for two years.

but the external epithelium proliferates and lines the cavity with epithelial cells that will secrete nacre.

We said earlier that nacre (or mother-of-pearl) is made of protein and calcium carbonate crystals called aragonite. Once the pearl sack is formed, the nacre secreted by the epithelium begins to be deposited in concentric layers from 0.5 to 1 micron thick. Each day an average of three or four such layers is secreted, the thickness of nacre secreted over a two year period varying greatly from one oyster to another. Starting with a nucleus 7.5 millimeters (about 1/4 inch) in diameter, an oyster can produce pearls 8 to 11 millimeters (11 mm. = 1/2 inch) in diameter and even as large as 12 millimeters.

When the surgical incision heals rapidly and quickly, a perfectly round pearl is formed. If the incision remains open while the nacre is being deposited, we get an elongation resulting in a pearl that is pear-shaped. Sometimes the nacre is secreted in an irregular fashion and this forms a baroque pearl. Secretion of nacre that is irregular but systematic will make a circled pearl, i.e., a pearl containing one or more grooves that form parallel circles. We don't know why this last phenomenon occurs, as it does in about 30 percent of the cases, nor how it can be prevented. My personal hypothesis is that the pearl rotates in its pearl sack. If the rotation has no definite axis and rotates in all directions, the pearl can become perfectly spherical. If the rotation takes place around an axis whose extension is through the incision, we have a drop or pear-shaped pearl. This rotation on an axis also explains certain defects such as when we see a hole or pin prick with a comet-like tail, which could very well be the beginning of a complete circle like those we find on the circled pearls.

During the two year period when the pearls are being formed, the oysters have to be watched constantly. The platforms are checked about once a week. What is there to fear?
• Predators, the foremost being man, the most dangerous predator. Thefts are not unusual.
• Pollution, which necessitates the relocation of the farm.
• Parasites, such as the *cliona* sponge and the *lithophagus* bivalve mollusk, both of which bore into the shells. Also algae, and spats of other shells. If these parasites exist in any number, the oysters must be taken out of the water and cleaned.

• Hurricanes, which can carry away oysters (and other things, such as houses). The platforms must be deep enough under the water. During the two year waiting period, work on the pearl farm goes on as usual. The next grafting season is prepared for without waiting to harvest the pearls planted the year before. There are buildings to be built, enlarged, equipped or improved; boats to be caulked and painted; new platforms readied for the young oysters that have grown big enough to be pierced and hung on the ropes, and so on. Let's look now at the organization of a pearl farm.

Pearl farms

A pearl farm can be compared to other farms as we know them. We can say that a pearl farm is a combination stock farm and agricultural farm. Its livestock is oysters; its crop is pearls.
A pearl farm consists of:
— Land acreage and the waters of the adjacent lagoon.
— An installation on land.
— An installation under water.
— Equipment.
— Livestock.
— Crops being grown.

The foremost consideration about a pearl farm is its location. It must be on a lagoon where oysters are already growing or where they have

Tahitian women preparing the wire cylinders inside which the oysters will be hung.

1

4

2

5

3

6

7

8

9

10

grown in their natural state in the past, free from sickness and in considerable numbers.

In French Polynesia, this means either the Tuamotu Archipelago or the Gambier Islands. These two locations have the right kind of lagoons: lagoons that are not too big whose waters are not too stormy, where there is no break in the reef or only a single, fairly narrow pass so that tides and ocean currents are not too strong — lagoons where pearls, whether natural or cultured, grow in satisfactory numbers and colors.

Lagoons that are not too far from Tahiti, so that they are easy to reach and easy to supply.

Once we have found that perfect atoll, we have to pick the right location for our farm: a spot sheltered from the wind, not too close to the pass through the reef so that currents won't be a problem, and with a coral rather than a sandy bottom.

After that we have to find acreage that is for sale or for long-term lease, and that's where our troubles begin. Land in Polynesia is often bequeathed on an indivisible basis and it can be difficult to get the numerous co-owners to agree to anything. Even when a legal solution appears to have been found, that doesn't mean the deal actually will go through.

However, let's suppose that we have managed to buy a few acres. Generally they will consist of a strip of land, about 100 to 300 yards wide, between the lagoon and the ocean. Probably the terrain is planted with coconut palms, overgrown with heavy brush, and populated by mosquitoes and what the Tahitians call *nonos* ("no-see-ems"), the tiny flies whose bites are more painful and slower to heal than a mosquito bite.

We will have to remove enough brush to clear a construction site and also clear out the mosquito and *nono* breeding grounds. As owner or lessor of property, we will have to obtain a maritime concession from the Territorial Government; to get that, we need the approval of the local authorities, authorizations from the Department of Fisheries (EVAAM) and the Assessor's office, etc... The administrative formalities are tedious, but when we have our clearance, the last step is to pay a very reasonable tax bill. (Some of us have wished they would raise the taxes a bit and speed up the formalities.)

Once the construction site is ready, we can begin building on land and in the water.

Land buildings

• First, we need a warehouse to store all our material: diving equipment, air tanks, compressors, ropes, buoys, mesh wiring, metal pipe, lumber, cement, etc.

• Second, a workshop to house a generator, soldering equipment, construction tools for other land buildings and the platforms that will go in the lagoon, material for the repair and upkeep of boats and motors.

• Third, housing for the permanent staff, plus a cistern to collect rain water, and also a shallow well. On a coral atoll one usually finds an aquifer of fresh or only slightly brackish water stored just above the infiltration of salt water. Solar electricity which is captured by photo-electric cells and stored in batteries to give us light and refrigeration.

• Fourth, two or three bungalows (Tahitian *fares*) roofed with palm branches, where the temporary employees can sleep at night.

Boats

Boats and a kind of catamaran, a platform mounted on two pontoons, are needed almost

1

2

3

4

LIST OF PEARL FARMS

COMPANY	ISLAND
ANUANURARO PERLES	ANUANURARO
TAHITI PERLES	MANGAREVA
POLYNESIE PERLES	MARUTEA-SUD
SOCIETE PERLIERE DE MANIHI	MANIHI
TUAMOTU PERLES	HIKUERU
PACIFIC PERLES	ARATIKA
PATONU PERLES	ARATIKA
SOCIETE "POE ITI"	ARUTUA
S.E.P.T.	MANIHI
SOCIETE Paul YU	MANIHI
VAIMAREVA POE	TAKAROA
SOCIETE GIAU	MANIHI
ROYAL TAHITIAN PEARL	MANIHI

immediately to get around the lagoon and to transport material for the underwater construction.

Underwater construction

This next job consists of two steps:
— Building the underwater platforms.
— Setting up a "park" in shallow water, where the young oysters will be kept temporarily while waiting to be drilled and hung from the crosspieces of the platforms.

Laboratory

Constructed as earlier described, this "grafting shack" serves also for the cleaning, manipulating, and piercing of the oysters.

Personnel

A pearl farm operates with a permanent staff of from three to five employees, depending on its size. During grafting, harvesting and construction periods, enough temporary employees are hired to easily double the staff, and this doesn't include the Japanese technicians who do the grafting.

Very few Polynesians are able to perform the grafting operation successfully. There are several reasons for this:
— The Japanese technicians are jealous of the secrets of their craft.

— At least 10,000 oysters must be sacrificed to produce a trained technician.
— Few Polynesians are willing to accept the discipline and concentration required to work at grafting all day long.
Polynesians certainly are skillful enough with their hands to master the technique and a few, such as Petero at Manihi, are as good as any Japanese.
In fairness to the Japanese, we must recognize that their training in marine biology gives them the know-how to manage the activities of the farm, and above all their industry and reliability count for a great deal. It's no easy task to operate on 25 to 35 oysters an hour, eight

PEARL COOPERATIVES

NAME	NUMBER OF MEMBERS
AHE	70
TIARE MANIHI	75
AHERE MANIHI	59
POE RAVA/TAKAPOTO	117
RIKITEA	62
TAKAROA	42
KAUA ROA/MAKEMO	53
RAUTINI/ARUTUA	23
KAUKURA	33
APATAKI	36
HIKUERU	28
FARATAHI ITI/MAROKAU	44
POE PARAU/TAKAPOTO	61
TAKUME	15
TEMURIAVAI/RARAKA	8
HITIANAU/KATIU	22
TAENGA	13
AMANU	16
POE RAGI/HAO	11
POE TAMARIKI VAHITU/ TAKAROA	26
MANIARO/AHE	22
TAIOEOE/MAKEMO	19
HIPOTI/TAKAPOTO	28
TIARE KAHAIA/MANIHI	14
TARAIRE/MANIHI	12
POROPORONUI/AHE	18
AHERE TAKAPOTO	15
POE RAU/TAKAPOTO	20
TAKU POE/TAKAPOTO	18
HEIARII/TAKAROA	10
TAMARA/MAKEMO	11
VAIROTOARIKI/HIKUERU	13
TIVERUROA/HIKUERU	7
POEHEVA NUI/MAKEMO	20
TAKU/RIKITEA	20
TAHOERAA TAMARII FAAITE	8
MANIHI NUI	13
TEOROMEA/MANIHI	14
GATAVAKE/RIKITEA	22
RUMAREI/RIKITEA	13
KARORUA/RIKITEA	14

Total: 40 cooperatives 1,145 members

Preceding double page:

1 - A general view of an underwater platform.

2 - Periodically Pitori Faura makes a careful check on the pearl oysters.

3 - Closeup underwater view of cylinders hanging from a platform.

4 - Checking the platform.

hours a day, day after day, with only a five minute cigarette break once an hour. Very few Polynesians are willing to keep their noses to the grindstone in that fashion, even for a high salary.

We have taken a tour of a medium-sized pearl farm, one that grafts between 15,000 and 20,000 oysters a year. A private company with all its personnel on salary has to graft at least 10,000 oysters to make a profit. A man who manages his own farm can get by on a smaller scale.

The inhabitants of the Tuamotus have formed cooperatives that are assisted by the Department of Fisheries (EVAAM) and given low interest loans by SOCREDO, which ensures repayment of its loans by holding public pearl auctions in October of each year.

In view of the current enthusiasm for pearl farming in Polynesia, where farms are multiplying at a great rate, I think it may be useful to review the difficulties commonly faced by those who invest in such farms:

1. Finding land. No need to go again into the problem of indivisibility and the more subtle problem of family members who refuse to accept a perfectly legal sale or lease.

2. Recruiting personnel. On an atoll where there usually is only one small village, and that one often torn by political or family quarrels, hiring can be difficult.

3. The owner's problem of staying neutral and

3

1 - Still in their cylinder, pearl oysters grafted two years earlier are taken from the water.

2 - Closeup of oysters in cylinder, showing "pipi" spats attached to them.

3 - Oyster sacrificed to show the pearl inside the gonad.

4 - Japanese technican opening the oyster.

5 - Inside the half-opened oyster we can glimpse a pearl.

6 - An instrument moves the tissues aside to display the pearl.

4

1

2

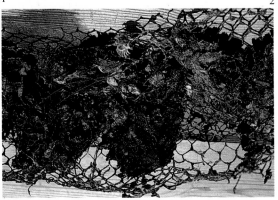

5

6

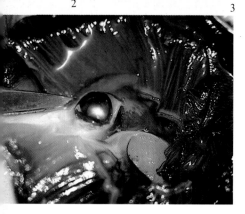

1 - Pearl inside its pearl sack.

2 - The technican uses scissors careful-ly to open the pearl sack...

3 - ...and gently pushes the pearl out of the sack.

4 - After so many years of waiting and hoping, at last we have a pearl!

5 - Closeup view of the pearl still enveloped in the pearl sack.

trying to remain friends with everyone. Theft, particularly common on certain islands, can be provoked as much by ill will as by desire for the merchandise.

4. Distance. Airline and maritime schedules have a considerable influence on the cost of doing business.

5. Administrative delays, authorizations, concessions. These often can delay a needed loan and result in hardships and the loss of precious time.

6. Regular supply of oysters. A prospective owner must be sure of a regular oyster supply before even thinking of building a

---

The following example is taken from the *Journal de Tahiti*, June 22, 1972, but the problems Koko Chase faced on Manihi atoll could easily happen today.

In every atoll, where people are stubborn and quirks of personality are well defin-ed, there are quarrels between certain in-dividuals and rivalries between certain families. In Takapoto the difficulties were minimized because of the form of the cooperative, but in Manihi the rivalries have degenerated to a point where people say "no" just to disagree with their neighbor. Add to that the natural distrust that Paumotus feel for outsiders and you wind up with the unholy mess we have in Manihi.

Like every other atoll, Manihi has the right to haul in a certain tonnage of oysters. After that limit is reached, diving is illegal for a five-year period in order to give the oysters time to repopulate the lagoon. The Manihi Pearl Company promised to buy the divers' entire catch, provided the oysters were young enough. The inhabitants of Manihi, however, are systematically bring-ing in very big, old oysters, not suited for making half-pearls but perfect for breeding since they are in their maximum period of fertility. Is this the divers' sneaky way of showing their hostility toward the pearl farm in general, or toward the tavana or chief (who heads the co-op that works with the S.P.M.) in particular?

To prevent the impoverishment of the lagoon, the Department of Fisheries has of-fered to buy the big oysters in order to return them to the water. Everyone would come out a winner — the divers who would receive the same amount of money and the S.P.M. because the oysters would stay in the lagoon and make more oysters. But the divers refuse.

Would you believe Koko Chaze finally had to go and buy his oysters in the neighbor-ing atoll of Ahe?

---

pearl farm, and a contract with an oyster supplier is very risky. Above all, never pay in advance!

7. Delayed return on investment. Remember that it takes four or five years before the farm shows a profit.

8. Marketing. Selling the pearls after you have them in hand involves many trips, in-terviews and arrangements.

The pearl harvest

A first harvest is a time of temendous excite-ment but also a time of great anxiety. Will all the effort, the financial investment, the long three-year wait be crowned with victory? The few samples brought up at the end of a year and a half give some idea of the success rate and the quality of the pearls. Still, everyone is kept in suspense until the very end.

Later on, when the harvest takes place every year or every six months, the surprises are fewer and everyone knows more or less what to expect, but still it is an exceptional moment, full of intense activity and keen excitement at the sight of the pearls.

Gone is the time the oysters were simply open-ed and sacrificed, and the pearls removed if there were any. Now harvesting is much like grafting: the oysters are presented to the technician in the same way and he examines the interior of the shell for a pearl, clearly visi-ble through its transparent sack. If there is

no pearl sometimes there is a keshi, sometimes nothing at all.

The pearl is removed by the same kind of incision as the one used for grafting. A slight pressure helps deliver the pearl, which is immediately wiped off and rapidly examined. It is then given to a trusted individual who enters it in the accounts and stores it in a safe place, for this is the kind of precious substance which incites covetousness.

If the technician judges the oyster sufficiently young and healthy, he may insert a new nucleus in place of the pearl he has just removed.

This new operation, called a *regraft* or a *reimplantation*, is a fairly recent invention; it enables production in one year of a bigger pearl, but one that may not be flawless.

Regrafting is not practiced in all pearl farms. Whether regrafting can be done several times on the same oyster is still a question, and those in a position to answer are keeping mum. The young oysters that are in good health but have produced neither pearl nor keshi are sure to be regrafted, with a nucleus and epithelial fragment inserted exactly as they were in the first operation. Other oysters may be kept to make keshis and half-pearls. Those that are in bad shape or too old are sacrificed.

After the harvest

At the end of each day, the harvested pearls are examined. When taken from the oyster, a pearl is somewhat dull. It must be washed in fresh water and dried, then lightly polished, either by placing it in a drum containing wood fragments, which polish pearls as the drum revolves, or simply by rubbing it in a little fine salt. As soon as it is polished, a pearl takes on all its wonderful brilliance.

Examining a lot of pearls is always something of a disappointment to an amateur, however. It's only when you look at them one by one that they reveal their different colors and their beauty.

Each day a record is kept of the number of oysters opened and checked, the number regrafted, the number eliminated, and the number of pearls and keshis obtained. The initial success rate can be estimated daily, but it is only at the end of the harvest, when we know the number of pearls obtained compared to the number of oysters grafted two years earlier, that we can arrive at a definite figure. We must take into account not only the oysters that rejected the graft but also the mortality rate and possible thefts. For example, if in 1981, 10,000 oysters were grafted and in June

1 - Truly worthy of being called "black pearls," these magnificent specimens show off to perfection against a mother-of-pearl background.

2 - Pear-shaped pearls.

3 - Round pearls showing delicate nuances of color.

4 - Beautiful round pearls displayed on polished mother-of-pearls. Notice the incredible delicacy and diversity of color.

1

66

1983 the harvest was 3,000 pearls, our success rate is 30%.

What are the usual success rates? They range from 25% to 40%, rarely any higher. The results vary according to:
• Atoll. Some lagoons (e.g. Hikueru) show up to 50% mortality.
• Location within the same lagoon.
• The technician's skill. Some technicians have a higher mortality rate than others.
• Percentage of rejects. This varies greatly, again based on the skill of the technician. Once harvested, the pearls are examined and sorted according to their color and other characteristics.

Though pearls are very different from each other in both color and shape, nevertheless there are predominating colors that identify certain lots.

When a jeweler sees one lot of pearls from a certain pearl farm and a few months later is shown a second lot, he may comment, "These pearls are not the same as those you showed me last time." Even though grafted by the same technician and produced by the same oysters in the same lagoon, if the oysters grew in different parts of that lagoon, one lot may display a predominantly green color and the other a grayer tone.

3

2

4

1 & 2 - The author at home. During the preparation of this book, he learned how to examine and evaluate pearls — a difficult task, but a very rewarding one.

3 - Two absolutely perfect pearls, embodying the mystique and the beauty of Polynesia.

1

2

3

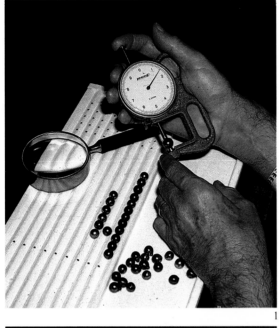

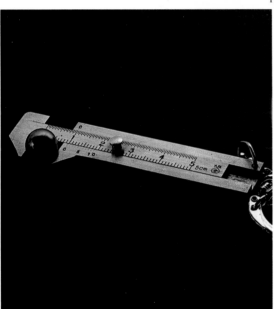

1 - Gauge (in millimeters) used for precise measurement of the size of a pearl.

2 - Slide calipers, an instrument useful to anyone interested in measuring pearls.

3 - Sieve-like apparatus with interchangeable bottoms showing perforations 8 to 12 mm. in diameter, used for the initial sorting for size.

4 - Scale for weighing pearls.

5 - Weighed and measured, the pearls are put in plastic bags with a label for recording their vital statistics. This type of bag is ideal for transporting and showing pearls.

THE CLASSIFICATION OF PEARLS

After the harvest, the pearls must be graded according to size, shape and brilliance, and any flaws in their surface noted. These judgments are necessary to allow an exact estimate of the value of the pearls so that they can be priced correctly and for the maximum amount.

The evaluation needs to be made by a competent, disinterested judge, since the seller naturally would have a tendency to overestimate their value and the buyer to underestimate it. The estimator examines the pearls in natural light, either in the morning or under an overcast sky with plenty of filtered light. These conditions will allow him or her to make a proper judgment according to three criteria:

I. SIZE

This first classification is easy. The pearls are passed through a sieve-like apparatus, something like a frying pan with a set of interchangeable bottoms perforated with round holes 11, 10, 9 and 8 millimeters in diameter.

The black pearls of Polynesia generally measure between 8 and 11 mm. with an occasional rare pearl as large as 12 or 13 mm. Their size depends not only on the size of the nucleus used (7 to 9 mm. being average), but also and chiefly on the thickness of the nacre secreted by the pearl oyster.

For pearls of fine quality, however, half a millimeter can make a big difference in the price, so we need a more precise measurement. After the first sort, then, each pearl is measured individually with a millimetric gauge which allows the measurement to be refined by half millimeters. A pearl classified as 10.5 mm., for instance, may actually be between 10.5 and 10.9 mm. in diameter.

II. SHAPE

Next, the pearls are reexamined individually and classified by shape, according to the following categories:

• **Perfectly round pearls**, i.e., those that will roll in every direction when they are placed on a flat surface. These are the most highly prized.

• **Pear-shaped or drop pearls** — The true pear-shape has a neck or extension at one end (corresponding to the incision where the nucleus was inserted), which distinguishes it from pearls that are merely semi-round. Egg-shaped pearls, without any neck, are also classified as drop pearls.

• **Buttons**, i.e., pearls which are rounded on one side, flatter on the other.

• **Baroque pearls**, i.e., those which are irregular in shape. They can be strange and interesting.

1 - Enlargement showing several beautiful round pearls and one exceptional, very dark pear-shaped pearl.

2 - A button-shaped pearl being removed from the oyster. Notice the flat bottom which gives this kind of pearl its name.

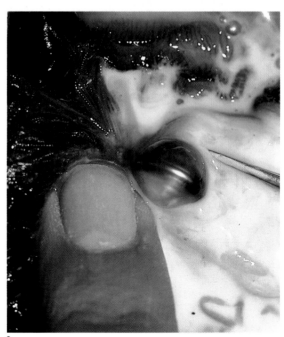

1

2

1

2

4

3

5

1 - A superb round pearl, superbly photographed.

2 - Drop pearls suitable for jewelry and especially for pendants. The slightly deformed neck of such pearls is easily hidden by a gold mounting, which can even be encrusted with diamonds.

3 - Baroque pearls, highly desired by manufacturing jewelers. Such pearls are set in beautiful mounted pieces and make very attractive necklaces.

4 - Circled pearls, very affordable, are widely used for necklaces and bracelets or as pendants worn on a long gold chain.

5 - Light-colored baroque and circled pearls, considered of lower quality.

1

Preceding double page:
Baroque pearls.

This page:

1 - An assortment of beautiful round pearls.

2 - An exceptional olive-shaped green pearl.

3 - Pearls graded B and C in quality. Pinpricks and other imperfections are clearly visible, yet such pearls have beautiful highlights.

4 - "Toi et moi" (you and I): a harmonious pair, one light, one dark.

5 & 6 - Exceptional in their coloration, these pearls with green, gold, and bronze highlights are far from the usual "black" pearl.

Facing page:

1 - A group of black pearls of perfect brilliance or luster.

2 - Each pearl is different, each unique.

• **Circled pearls** — These have one or more parallel furrows encircling the pearl perpendicular to its longer axis or its stem. This formation occurs rather frequently. Circled pearls are less highly valued but they make attractive necklaces and bracelets.

III. SURFACE

Finally, the surface of the pearl is judged. The estimator looks for flaws, using a magnifying glass if necessary, and checks three characteristics of the pearl:

• Brilliance — This is the first thing about a pearl that strikes the eye: its *luster* or brilliance, caused by the reflection of light from its satiny surface. Do not confuse this luster with the "water" seen in certain white pearls, which is caused by the fracture of light rays as they pass through the aragonite crystals; this phenomenon gives such pearls a kind of diaphanous radiance, and the more delicate the layers of nacre, the more "water" a pearl will have. Black pearls possess fairly thick layers of nacre and do not have this quality of water but display instead a luster. Looking at a black pearl should be like looking into a mirror.

• **Color** — This is the second most striking characteristic of a pearl. Color doesn't enter greatly into the estimation of a pearl's value because what constitutes a beautiful color is mainly a matter of taste. Nevertheless it is interesting to study the different nuances of color.

Since we call them "black" pearls, some people expect them to be fairly dark. It's true, some pearls really are black. But the color most characteristic of Polynesian pearls is a greenish black, called "fly wing" in French, *poe rava* in Tahitian, and "peacock" in English. Sometimes these green-black pearls have reddish highlights that recall the blend of colors found on the edges of the interior of a *Margaritifera* shell. Others are lighter in color, running the gamut of off-white, steel-gray, dark gray with brown or red highlights, and so on.

Gray pearls are fairly common and not too sought after, but again, that is a matter of taste and also of the way the pearl is mounted.

Sometimes the color is not uniform, being darker on one side than on the other.

Most unusual of all are the light-colored pearls that are definitely blue, green, pink, copper or gold. It is difficult to match or make pairs among these very attractive pearls because they are so rare.

2

4

5

3

6

1

2

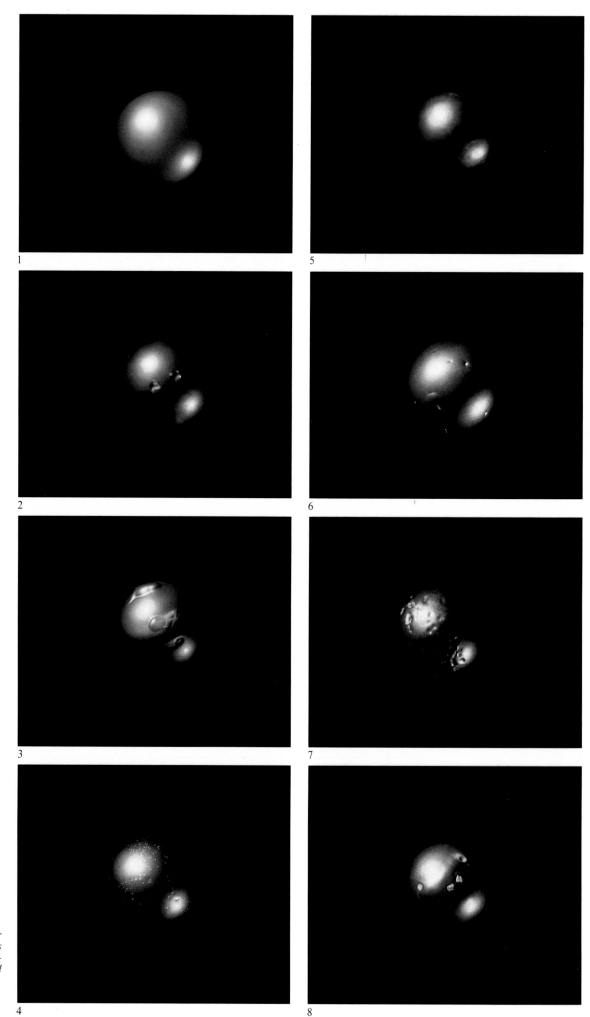

1 & 5 - Grade A round pearls.

2, 3, 4, 6, 7 & 8 - Grade C pearls, their flaws accentuated by the photographer's lighting. The percentage of such rejects depends on the technician's skill and the mood of the oysters.

• **Actual surface** — This is the third element to look for: the quality of the pearl's skin, so to speak. Is it perfectly smooth or are there tiny irregularities? This is a very important factor in classifiying pearls and determining their value. A microscopic hole called a pinprick is the most frequent flaw, followed by a tiny scratch or roughness which may mar the surface for 2 or 3 millimeters. Pits, even shallow ones that girdle the pearl cause it to be classified as "circled" and to bring a much lower price.

IV. GRADING

When the estimator has finished, he grades the pearls as follows:

• **By shape** — According to their shapes, pearls are classified as:

• **By surface** — Pearls are rated A, B, C, or D:

A. Pearls with a flawless skin and high brilliance. A pinprick or even a single, somewhat deeper flaw does not detract too

Round	R
Drop or pear-shaped	D
(Sometimes with a subclass of the pear-shaped that is called	
drop-round)	DR
Baroque	BRQ
Circled	CIRC
Button	BUT

much since the pearl must be pierced at the time it is mounted and the perforation will hide the flaw.

B. Pearls that are less brilliant and have two or three surface flaws.
C. Pearls that are somewhat dull or have shallow pinpricks or scratches.
D. Pearls that are definitely dull or marred by deeper flaws.

Scrap — Dull pearls with flawed surfaces, pearls in which the nucleus shows through the nacre, or circled pearls in which the pits are so deep that the nucleus is visible. They have no value and are just discarded.

• **By size** — Pearls are measured in millimeters, in increments of .5 millimeters. Thus two letters and a number give us a code

that allows a pearl to be described and assigned an approximate value. For example, a code of RA 10 means a round pearl of fine brilliance, with an almost perfect skin, measuring between 10 and 10.49 mm. in diameter. The percentage of pearls in each category varies, of course, from one pearl farm to another. Some farms produce a greater proportion of circled pearls, some more baroque shapes, and so on. Nevertheless, we can give the estimates shown below.

V. WEIGHTS

In Japan weight is constantly used to price white pearls, which are sold by the strand. Weight is also used for other fine pearls, which are weighed in "grains."
• One grain equals one-quarter of a carat (.05 gram or 5 centigrams).
• One carat equals one-fifth of a gram (20 centigrams).
Cultured pearls are weighed in units called "mommes."
• One momme equals 18.75 carats or 3.74 grams.

Round	20-30%
Drop or pear-shaped	30-40%
Circled	25-30%
Baroque	5-10%
Buttons	1-2%

Pearls rated A, B and C are found in approximately equal quantities. D are rare.

Sizes occur as follows:

12-13 mm.	1 or 2 per thousand
11	20 per thousand
10.5	5 per hundred
10	10 per hundred
9.5	25 per hundred
9	35 per hundred
8	25 per hundred

(Pearls from an oyster which has had a second operation are generally larger).

Due to their rarity and value, the Tahitian pearls are individually appreciated and their weight has little importance. In fact it does not give any indication of the size of the nucleus in relation to the diameter of the pearl.
However it can be used in the identification of each individual pearl whose shape, quality and size has already been determined. For instance a pearl DA 11 weighing 2.20 gr has lit-

tle chance of being confused or substituted with a similar pearl.

The specialist who grades the pearls must also match together pairs and keep similar pearls from each harvest to complete a necklace.

Other pearls produced in Polynesia

Besides the extremely rare natural fine black pearls and the cultured pearls that we have just discussed, there are two other kinds of pearls that occur as a byproduct of the pearl industry: keshis and blister pearls.

Keshis — These are small cultured pearls that result when only a fragment of epithelial tissue is grafted. Either the oyster rejects the nucleus or the technician decides at the onset of the graft that he wants to produce a keshi. He then omits the nucleus altogether, inserting only a piece of mantle in the pearl oyster. After a year or two, the result is a small pearl, usually baroque in form, displaying the same colors as natural or cultured pearls.

Blister pearls — These can be either natural or cultured pearls whose core contains organic matter which decomposes, producing gas that causes the pearl to swell or blister. The result is a large baroque pearl, very light weight because it was inflated from the inside, and sometimes containing opaque black patches of organic origin. Blister pearls, which generally are steel-gray, formerly were used as hatpins. Today imaginative jewelers use them to create original pieces.

Half-pearls — Another kind of cultured pearl produced by a different type of operation on the *Pinctada margaritifera* is called the half-pearl, referred to as *chicots* (meaning "stump") in French or *mabe* in Japanese, from the name of the black-winged *Pteria penguin* oyster which yields only half-pearls. (By extension, the term *mabe* is now used for all half-pearls.)

The technique for producing half-pearls is different from that used to make full pearls; it is also much simpler, which is the reason that half-pearls were obtained first in both Japan and Polynesia.

To produce a half-pearl, the technician opens the oyster, gently pushes back the mantle and places a half-sphere (usually made of plastic) against the inner face of the shell, using a special glue to make it adhere. No graft is necessary. He then pulls the mantle back in place. At the end of a year, the foreign body

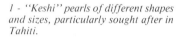

1 - "Keshi" pearls of different shapes and sizes, particularly sought after in Tahiti.

2 - An unusual blister pearl (from the collection of Giovanni Onorato, Milan).

3 - Half-pearl and two-thirds pearl, called "chicots" in French, "mabe" in Japanese. The grafting technician produces this kind of pearl by pushing the mantle of the oyster gently aside and gluing a half-sphere of plastic between the oyster and its shell. It takes only one year for nacre to cover the foreign body, which is then cut away, yielding a half-pearl.

1

2

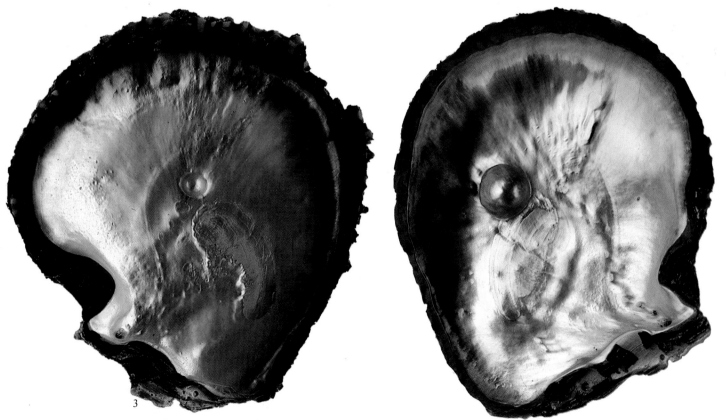

3

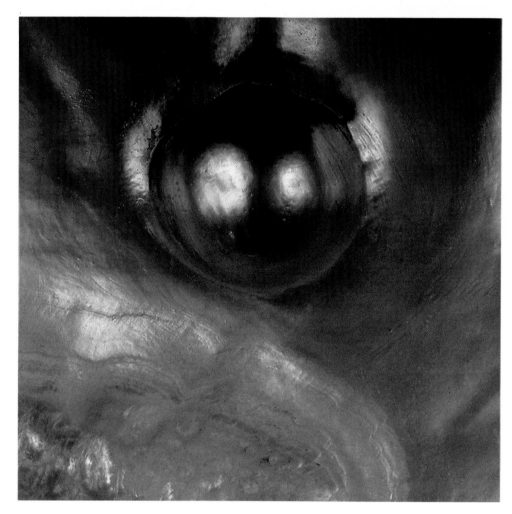

A beautiful half-pearl.

1

1 & 2 - "Pipi" (baby) pearls of different sizes, displayed in the shells of the Pinctada maculata *oyster that produces them.*

2

is covered with a layer of nacre of the same color as the mother-of-pearl on the interior of the shell around the formation and, once it is cut out of the oyster, we have a half-pearl whose surface can be as smooth and vari-colored as any black pearl. Half-pearls are much used in jewelry as pendants, rings and earrings. One can also produce two-third pearls by the same technique.

Generally older oysters are chosen for the production of half-pearls, whether or not those oysters have already been used to make full pearls.

Pipi pearls — *Pipi* means "baby" in Tahitian, and we mustn't neglect to mention pipi pearls (pronounced "peepee"). These are small, round, natural pearls which measure 3-4 millimeters in diameter and are yellow, orange, or honey-colored. They are produced by the *Pinctada maculata* oyster. These little pearl oysters are common in Polynesia, especially in closed lagoons.

The pearls are harvested by letting the oysters rot in a basket enclosed by wire mesh. The basket is then washed in sea water and the pearls collected in a fine sieve.

The small number of *pipi* pearls collected limits them to the local market, where their cost is reasonable and they are used to make nice delicate jewelry.

It is to be hoped that their market value will not go up, for unless the little oysters are raised by organized farming and systematically harvested, they will rapidly become extinct. For the time being, the limited market for pipi pearls wouldn't appear to justify such efforts. (However, the first effort, perhaps, should be to find them a more poetic name.)

Production and sale of Tahiti's black pearls

The production of black pearls has increased steadily since 1972.

Beginning in 1983 they became the leading export of the Territory of French Polynesia. Their export value is stated at 700 million Pacific francs, but in reality that figure must be more like a billion CFP because the official figure doesn't include all the pearls, whether loose or mounted as jewelry, that tourists buy and take home with them.

The retail market for pearls in Tahiti is a busy one!

However, a billion Pacific francs — $6,000,000 in 1985 U.S. dollars — represents approximately 150,000 pearls, which would weigh 200 kilograms or 440 pounds. Compare that figure to Japan's annual production of 40 or 50 *tons* and you get an idea of how small Tahiti's pearl industry really is.

Even if the Tahitian pearls are not appreciated as much as the white pearls produced in Japan, because they are not yet as widely recognized, it still is obvious that the market for black pearls has not reached a saturation point.

Commercialization of black pearls

A few big companies, such as Assael International and Golay & Buchel, have been dealing in black pearls for years and have contributed a great deal to making the international market aware of them. The Japanese, who also are enthusiastic buyers, are the only nationality that has participated with local buyers in the pearl auctions put on by the cooperatives.

Tahiti exports her pearls to three main trading centers: the United States (particularly New York), Switzerland and Japan. From there they are distributed all over the world, but it is difficult to determine which countries buy the most and in what quantities.

When all is said and done, the pearls of Tahiti are relatively unknown.

Outside of the three centers mentioned above, most jewelers have never heard of black pearls or, if they have, they don't know the difference between pearls that are naturally black and those that are dyed. If they do know, many of them will keep the information to themselves because dyed pearls cost much less and consequently carry a much higher profit margin.

Not all of the pearls produced in Polynesia are exported. Some of the larger farms retail jewelry through their own shops in Papeete. There are many manufacturing jewelers in both Tahiti and Moorea; some have luxury boutiques, others are simple artisans working at home.

All of them are in love with the vari-colored Polynesian pearls and compete in ways of using them in jewelry that ranges from the simplest designs to the most sumptuous.

THE PROMOTION
OF TAHITIAN PEARLS

Why aren't the black pearls of Tahiti better known and more in demand around the world?

- For one thing they are a relatively new product, available commercially for only the last ten years, and pearl production is still so small that it hardly justifies the large investment that would be required to promote the product effectively. The demand still exceeds the supply, so there is no problem selling fine quality pearls and even those that are not so fine.
- Thus far the promotion has been chiefly through magazine and newspaper articles written at the invitation of the owners of the main pearl farms. Big companies buy the pearls and sell them to their own clientele, but, as far as I can see, don't do much to open up new markets. Otherwise more professional jewelers would know about black pearls and want to sell them.

Take the case of a jewelry shop in one of the largest hotels in Los Angeles, where only dyed black pearls were on display. I asked the owner of the shop, ''Why don't you carry the authentic black pearls from Tahiti?'' ''There's no demand for them,'' he said. My reply was, ''It seems to me it's up to you to display this beautiful new product and educate your customers about it.''

- The Japanese, who buy and sell quite a lot of black pearls, have no reason to promote Tahiti's pearls over the white ''South Seas pearls,'' much less over their own domestic product.

Therefore, instead of being satisfied with selling through their established outlets, it's up to the Tahitian producers to do the necessary prospecting for new markets. The local government could second their efforts by a strong public relations campaign, as was done for the tourist industry.

But I think, above all, the government's role should be to defend Tahiti's authentic black pearls against the widespread dyed imitations. In a shop in Paris that specializes in pearls, I saw genuine black pearls and dyed black pearls displayed side by side, with no printed information in the display case to explain the difference between them. If that is possible in France, which after all has close ties to Tahiti, what can be expected anywhere else? Friends of mine from Hong Kong, for instance, who bought black pearls in Tahiti, told me rather coldly that they could get them much cheaper at home. Obviously no one there had bothered to tell them why.

Other pearl-producing countries encourage the exportation of their product, whereas in Polynesia a 3% tax is imposed on the export of pearls. Why not dedicate part of that tax to a promotional public relations campaign for Tahiti's black pearls? It would be an investment that would certainly pay for itself.

BEWARE OF COUNTERFEITS

Buying a black pearl

We are not talking here about natural black pearls, which are now exceedingly scarce, but about cultured black pearls. Here are my suggestions:

First, be sure to buy an authentic black pearl, not an imitation.

Dyed pearls

I don't recommend purchasing dyed pearls at all, but certainly you don't want to buy them

FRANCIS NANAI

Francis is a Tahitian, a dealer in black pearls and a man of the sea, European champion in underwater spear fishing and member of the French Underwater Spear Fishing Team for 13 years. Sports competition gave him a bent for travel and foreign languages.

Whereas the large pearl companies have dealers who have many contacts with the large jewelry concerns, the small pearl farms had no one to help with their smaller-scale marketing — to find interested jewelers and to generate interest in their product. Francis filled the bill. He is right at home among the small pearl farm owners and has succeeded in contacting customers for them. Courteous, discreet, a hard worker with a good sense of humor, Francis has the patience and perseverance of a champion. His career in black pearls should be a very successful one.

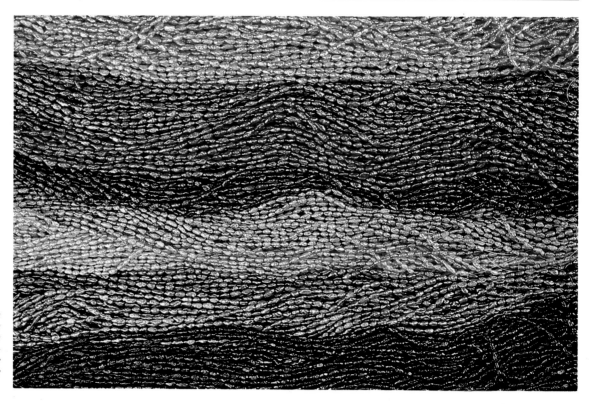

Biwa *fresh-water pearls dyed in various colors. These pearls are grown in China. Because of strict laws in Polynesia against the artificial coloring of pearls, pearls of this kind are never sold in Tahiti; it is against the law to import them.*

believing they are the genuine article.

To explain a little about pearls that are dyed black: they usually are pearls from Japan whose original color wasn't pleasing. In Japan such pearls normally are dried, then bleached in hydrogen peroxide; this treatment is allowed because it is more a matter of rendering the colors uniform and harmonious than of altering them. After bleaching, pearls that are still yellowish or too cream-colored — in other words, still unattractive — are then dyed black. There are two processes for blackening a pearl:

— Bombardment with cobalt gamma rays. Aside from the danger of working with cobalt, this process results in a brownish color that is not very satisfactory.

— Dyeing with silver nitrate and other mineral salts in a solution of alcohol. The exact formula is a secret jealously guarded by those who use it.

Now, how can you recognize dyed pearls?

— Fortunately, dyes never have yielded a color — and the variety of colors — that can compare with the real thing. Dyed pearls usually have a purplish tinge that is easily recognizable, and rarely do they have the luster of authentic cultured black pearls.

— You can tell if a pearl is dyed by scratching it lightly. A genuine black pearl gives off a whitish dust, while a dyed pearl gives off black dust.

— Since dyed pearls come from Japan, they seldom are larger than 8 millimeters in diameter, whereas Tahitian pearls usually are bigger. Dyed black pearls of larger size probably are "South Seas pearls" or big lackluster fresh water pearls. South Seas pearls sell for almost the same price as authentic black pearls, so there isn't much incentive to dye them.

Your best guarantee is to buy your pearls from a reputable jewelry shop, which is required by law to give you a certificate of authenticity or, alternatively, will state on the bill whether you have bought a "natural black cultured pearl" or a "cultured pearl dyed black." According to law, the word "pearl" may be used only for *natural* pearls. For cultured pearls, even those without a nucleus, the term "cultured pearls" must be specified, and if the pearls have been artificially colored, the word "dyed" (*teintee* in French) must appear on the bill.

If you think you have been sold a bill of goods, consult an expert or write to:

Laboratoire de la Chambre du Commerce
2, Place de la Bourse
75003 Paris, France

In the United States, write to the Gemological Institute of America.

Imitation pearls

Just a word about imitation pearls. These generally are balls of glass or sometimes

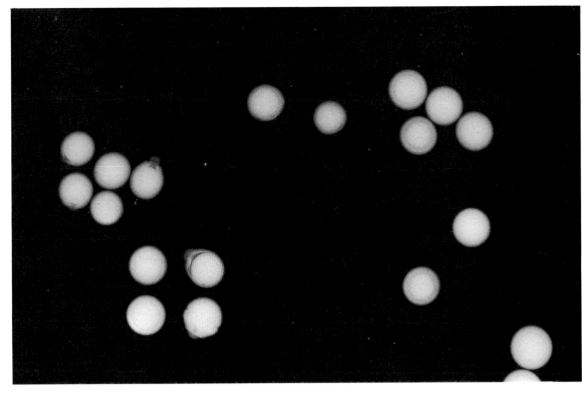

X-rays of black pearls, in which are visible the nucleus and outer layer of nacre that form the pearl.

plastic, either solid or hollow, which have been dipped in an ''Oriental essence'' made of fish scales. The easy way to recognize an imitation pearl is to rub it gently against your teeth; an imitation will slide smoothly, whereas a cultured pearl will grate. The island of Marjorca, off the coast of Spain, specializes in the manufacture of imitation pearls, the ''*Majorica*'' trademark being the best known. As far as I know, there are no imitation black pearls, and in any case, there is an international law which requires the label or bill to always state clearly ''imitation pearls.''

Some necklaces made of hematite, an iron ore compound, look from a distance rather like black pearls, but the illusion vanishes when they are seen close up.

Immature pearls

There is one problem that worries the jewelers in Tahiti, who are in a position to study and compare black pearls: the thinness of the layer of nacre covering some of the pearls offered to them for sale. Apparently certain pearl farmers are in such a hurry to recover their investment that they don't allow enough time for the pearls to form. Pearls harvested prematurely of course won't have as much nacre as those that are allowed their full period of growth.

Another problem: formerly a big pearl meant a good thickness of nacre, but with the supergrafts used today, size is no guarantee. If you are buying a big expensive pearl, you have the right to ask for an X-ray of it which will enable you to see and measure the thickness of the layers of nacre surrounding the nucleus. One millimeter of nacre is a minimum for a good pearl.

WHERE SHOULD YOU BUY YOUR BLACK PEARLS?

Tahiti certainly is the best place.
— You are at the source of supply. If you wish, you have the possibility of buying unmounted pearls direct from the producers.
— You have the widest possible choice.
— If you prefer to buy pearls already mounted as jewelry, the jewelers in Tahiti are accustomed to working with black pearls and can offer you a wide variety of mountings, from the simplest to the most elegant.
— You can be sure of getting genuine black pearls. It is illegal to import dyed pearls into Tahiti.

If you do not have an opportunity to visit Tahiti, you can buy your black pearls from the best jewelers and, more especially, from those that specialize in pearls. These specialists will provide you with their guarantee that you have selected authentic, natural color, cultured pearls of Polynesian origin — the most beautiful black pearls in the world. If you live in a small town or city, you have every right to ask your jeweler to look into black pearls. It will be easy for him to find a wholesaler who will send him a consignment of Tahitian pearls, allowing him to add something new and different to the assortment of jewelry he offers his clientele and to try his creativity on distinctive designs. Let him be the first in your city, perhaps even in your state, to feature black pearls. I'm sure he will have no reason to regret it.

WHY AND HOW TO CHOOSE A BLACK PEARL

The black pearl is a new product, sought after for its contrast with white pearls and so far imitated only as to color.

For a long time pearls were considered passe, but now they are back in style — a good reason to buy one or more black pearls. When you give someone a black pearl mounted as a pendant or in a ring or earrings, you have the satisfaction of knowing you are in the very forefront of fashion. And your pearl comes with a certificate of authenticity.

Black pearls usually are sold already mounted, particularly if the pearl is classified B or C. It's up to the jeweler to minimize any flaws and offer an attractive piece of jewelry at an affordable price.

Buying an unmounted pearl has one advantage, of course: you can see for yourself whether the pearl is flawless. A knowledgeable buyer can tell whether his selection is classified as an A, B, or C.

The mounting can be selected later on.

Black pearls go perfectly with every other kind of jewels, including white pearls, colored stones, and diamonds; they complement each other very well. Usually a black pearl is mounted in gold. Adding diamonds or other precious stones to the setting simply enhances the beauty of the pearl.

Even in a very expensive mounting, a pearl of superior quality will stand out because of its beauty and brilliance.

Approximate cost of black pearls

The price of a pearl naturally depends upon its quality and size.

The lowest quality pearls are sold in bulk to wholesalers, dealers and manufacturing jewelers at prices governed by the law of supply and demand. Nevertheless, bracelets consisting of a few keshis or circled pearls are a charming gift. At the time this book was published, baroque pearls, also very nice as pendants or worn on a long gold chain, were selling for $60-180 dollars U.S. (10,000 to 30,000 CFP)[1]. The price of the setting is determined, of course, by the price of gold and the amount of gold used.

Pear-shaped or drop pearls rated B, 8 to 9 mm. in size, were selling for between $130-165 U.S. (20,000 to 25,000 CFP). The same pearls, 10 to 11 mm., sold for $180-335 U.S. (30,000 to 50,000 CFP). Pear-shaped pearls rated A in quality (i.e., flawless) were priced at about $260-800 U.S. (40,000 to 120,000 CFP).

A superb round pearl of A quality, 10 to 11.5 mm., costs between $670-1,340 U.S. (100,000 to 200,000 CFP).

Now the sheik who went through Tahiti recently and bought 30 million CFP worth of pearls ($200,000 U.S.) might have been given a discount (knowing how Arabs like to bargain). But if you aren't keeping a harem, just looking for something nice for your wife or sweetheart, the most beautiful gift you could give her would be a 50-pearl graduated necklace of Grade A pearls of matching color, 8 to 12 mm. in size. Cost: between $23,300-28,000 U.S. (3.5 - 4.2 million CFP) — for the pearls only, price of the clasp not included. Or if she would rather have a choker of 48 10 mm. pearls, the price would be only $18,000-21,700 U.S. (2.7-3.4 million CFP).

Black pearls as an investment

Aside from the pleasure of wearing a beautiful object or giving a beautiful gift, is a black pearl a worthwhile investment?

Tahitian black pearls are a new thing and their production has entered a stage of full expansion. If they are better promoted and more carefully protected, the market for them may show rapid growth.

There is no difficulty in selling black pearls at the going rate. So far the demand exceeds the supply and the market is far from being saturated.

[1] *At the time of publication, $1.00 U.S. = 150 CFP.*

In Tahiti, rising prices have compensated for the falling value of the Pacific franc. Compared to the price of other precious stones at the big jewelry sales, the price of black pearls keeps going up.

Assuming that the increasing supply eventually catches up with the demand, the most beautiful pearls will still conserve their value because they are so rare. In spite of its high price, a flawless, brilliant, big pearl of a beautiful color, whether round or pear-shaped, will always find a buyer. Pearls of lesser quality, on the other hand, will sell for less money.

Working with pearls as jewelry

More than imagination is required to create beautiful jewelry using black pearls. The jeweler must be able to perform several operations.

1. Peeling — This is optional and can only be done by specialists skilled in pearls. It involves removing several layers of flawed nacre, much as you would peel an onion, in order to increase the quality of the pearl's surface. Naturally the size and weight of the pearl are reduced, but if the operation is successful, the quality of the new surface more than compensates. On the other hand, if the nucleus is exposed, the pearl is a total loss. Peeling calls for experience and is an exceptional procedure which is done by only a few men in the world.

2. Piercing — When pearls are to be strung in a necklace, they must be pierced through the center. If there are any defects, such as a fairly deep pit, the perforation should be made through the defect. The Japanese have perfected piercing machines that can center the perforation exactly.

3. Mounting — To mount pearls in a pendant, ring or earrings, the pearl is perforated to its center and a delicate, slightly notched stalk is inserted. This stalk and a super-strength glue ensure a secure mounting.

The setting can be made even stronger by putting glue in the perforation and lining it with silver. When the lining is dry, it is lightly threaded and the stalk, also covered with glue, is then screwed into the lining.

If for any reason the pearl has to be removed from its setting, a special solvent for super-strength glue must be used. There is always a risk that the pearl may break when it is removed.

Caring for your pearls

Pearls are precious objects. It is worth making a little effort, because of both their intrinsic beauty and their monetary value, to keep them in perfect condition.

Remember that pearls are produced by a living organism. They are made of calcium carbonate crystals which react to acid, and they also contain protein and water, so they are subject to dehydration and cracking.

Pearls are not as hard as precious stones. On the Mohs scale, a diamond has a hardness of 10 degrees, a ruby 9, an emerald 7.5, jade 6.5, turquoise 6, and pearls only 3.5 to 4.5, the same as coral. Your fingernail (rating 2.5) cannot scratch a pearl, but a knife (5.5) can. Therefore protect your pearls from direct contact with the rest of your jewelry and other hard objects that can mar them.

Because of the conchioline which binds the aragonite crystals, pearls will bounce, not break, if you drop them on cement.

Pearls contain 2.23% water in the conchioline protein substance. They will burn at 350°C. (662° F.) when the aragonite crystals become calcite but become dry enough to crack at a considerably lower temperature. If exposed for a long time to a hot, dry environment, they may also become dehydrated. It is advisable to moisten them from time to time by soaking them in either fresh or slightly salted water.

If cracking has occurred, Leonard Rosenthal has advised putting the pearls into a fatty substance, after which, he says, "the cracking generally won't recur."

Speaking of fatty substances, it is often said that wearing pearls helps preserve their brilliance. I believe the sebaceous glands in the skin lubricate the pearls and make them shine, preventing dehydration just as face creams prevent dry skin.

On the other hand, some people have an acid perspiration which is harmful to pearls. The acidity attacks the calcium carbonate crystals and will first dull the pearls, then little by little cause them to lose the layers of nacre that cover the nucleus. A jeweler of my acquaintance told me of one of his clients whose perspiration had caused the disappearance of the nacre and half the nucleus of a pearl that she wore as a pendant. People who have a problem with acid perspiration would be well advised to wear their pearls over clothing, so that there is no direct contact with the skin. Besides acid, avoid dishwashing and laundry detergents. These contain bleaching agents that may discolor your pearls. Also be careful with sprays that might affect them. Make it a practice to rinse and dry your pearls before you put them away, especially in hot weather. Occasionally, after drying them, put a few drops of olive oil on a chamois skin and wipe them off; the oil will restore their brilliance and keep them from drying out. If a pearl is in really bad condition and has a dead look, or if it is scratched or shows evidence of having been hit, a specialist can polish the pearl, restoring its luster and perfect smoothness.

Jewelry made with pearls

A jeweler who works with pearls has to combine the imagination and talent of a designer with the skill of a manufacturing jeweler. The photographs on the following pages show you some of the pieces designed and executed by:
Marchak, rue de la Paix in Paris
Giovanni Onorato, Via della Spiga in Milano
And in Tahiti:
Polynesie Perles,
Pierre Mourareau,
Michel Fouchard,
"Perles"

My thanks to all for their kind cooperation.

Because my background is in science and I have very little inclination toward the supernatural, I have not yet mentioned the supposed magic power of the pearl, which has been an object of desire but also of fear... for isn't it a sin to covet absolute beauty?

Cleopatra, in the presence of Mark Anthony, dissolved her most beautiful pearl in vinegar and drank down the concoction, thereby showing her disdain for wealth, her penchant for flamboyant gesture, and her faith in the healing properties of "aqua perlata" — properties which at that time had an aura of magic. As a physician, I do not see anything supernatural in what she did; rather in that gesture I see an empirical recognition, enhanced by an aura of mystery, of the properties of Calcium, a mineral essential to mental and physical health.

As one who serves beauty, I would have liked to be more eloquent in praising the beauty of the pearl, that living and fragile jewel which better than any other, accompanies and enhances the beauty of woman.

And although I am not of a religious turn of mind, I shall end with a citation from the Bible:

"Again, the kingdom of heaven is like unto a merchant man, seeking goodly pearls, who, when he had found one pearl of great price, went and sold all that he had, and bought it."

Doctor Lintilhac

Gallery

II

IV

V

VIII

X

XI

XII

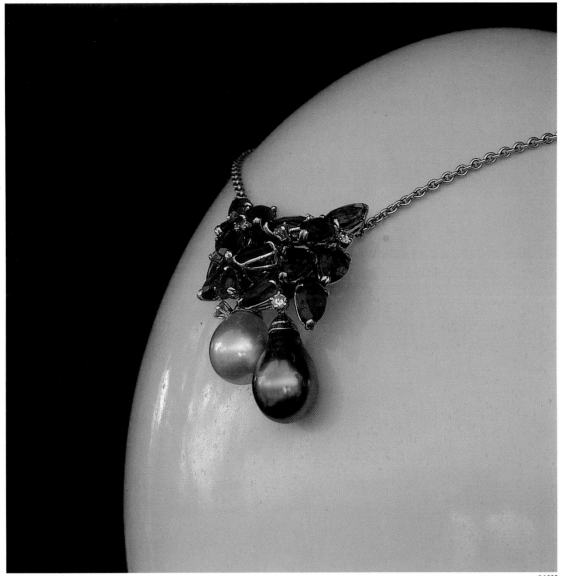

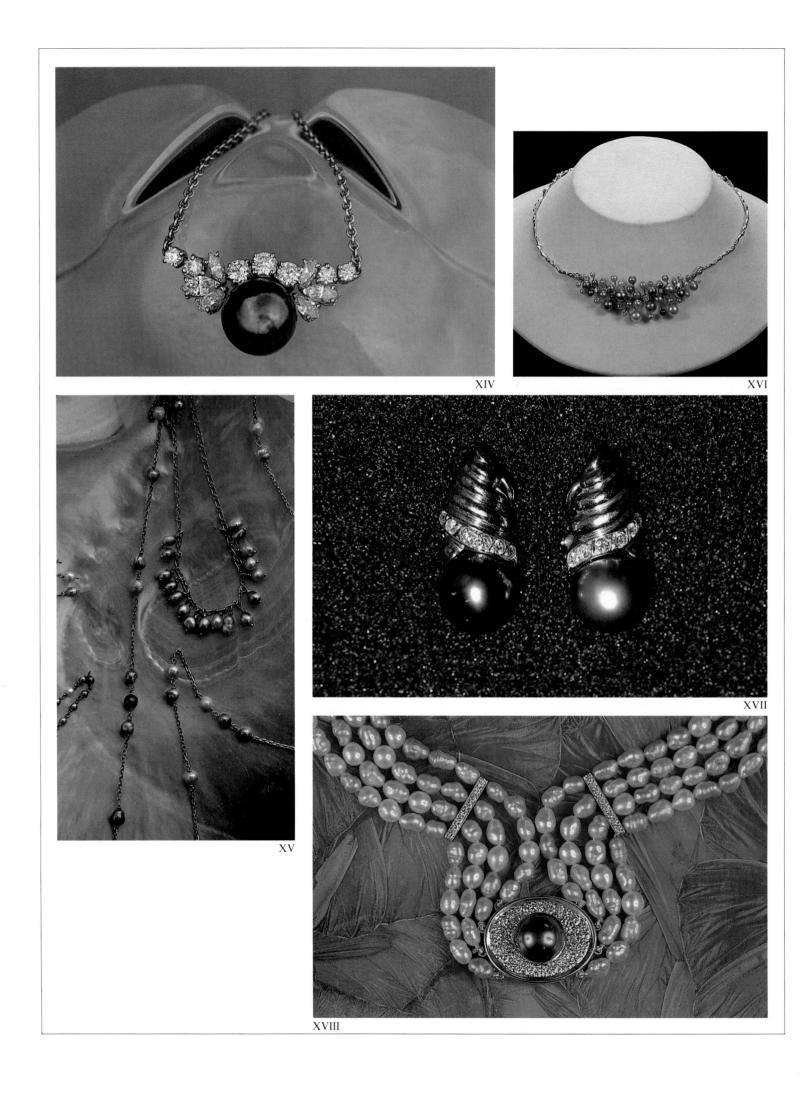

XIV

XVI

XV

XVII

XVIII

XIX

XX

Gallery

I - Set of sumptuous gold and diamond jewelry with round, Grade A pearls 12.5 millimeters in size, worn by Madame Simone Lintilhac. *Each pearl of a different color can be considered as an example of the most beautiful hues obtained in Polynesia.*

Necklace, bracelet and earrings were designed and made by Pierre Mourareau *of Tahiti.*

The ring is by Jacques Verger, Marchak Jewelers, *Paris.*

II - Exquisite "toi et moi" (you and I) ring — one Tahitian white pearl and one black pearl in an embrace of diamonds. Mounting by Trio Pearl, Hong Kong.

III - Adlin wearing a magnificent double strand of decorated gold with forty-two Grade A round pearls, between 11.5 and 12 mm. in size, in harmonious shades of gray. Pierre Mourareau, Tahiti.

IV - Wanda displays an exceptional necklace of Tahitian black pearls of grade A quality separated by balls of gold. The pendant is a pear-shaped pearl surrounded by rubies and diamonds. Michel Fouchard, Tahiti.

V - Two grade A pearls, 12.5 mm. in size, set in a ring with gold and diamonds. One pearl is copper-colored with purplish highlights, the other an iridescent green. Marchak, Paris.

VI - Displayed against the black sand of Tahiti, we see a variation of the necklace shown on page 89 in which the gold spiral has been enhanced by diamonds. Black and white pearls from Tahiti. Pierre Mourareau, Tahiti.

VII - A necklace of thirty-four alternating gray and black Grade A round pearls, 10 to 12 mm. The pearls are separated by delicate gold rings, some with natural finish, some set with diamonds. The pendant is a cabochon ruby encircled with diamonds. Polynésie Perles, Tahiti.

VIII - A twisted necklace of three strands of baroque pearls, each strand a different color: light gray, medium gray, and black. Made by "Perles" Jewelers, Tahiti.

IX - Necklace of keshi pearls strung on 18 carat gold. The contrasting colors are accented by diamonds; the necklace finishes with an olive-shaped pearl. The design illustrates the jeweler's remarkable skill, expressed in the harmonious arrangement of the pearls by size and color. Michel Fouchard, Tahiti.

X - A classic choker of 18 carat gold supporting a gold centerpiece "paved" with diamonds from which is suspended a round pearl, grade A, of 13 mm. attached to the pendant with a diamond. Polynésie Perles, Tahiti.

XI - "Skirted" ring encrusted with baguette diamonds. The round pearl is green, Grade A, 11 mm. and set in 18 carat gold. Pierre Mourareau, Tahiti.

XII - A "button" pearl, Grade A, 12 mm., black with green highlights, set in a bed of diamonds and gold suspended from an 18 carat gold chain. Polynésie Perles, Tahiti.

XIII - Two pear-shaped pearls, one lustrous white, the other black with bronze highlights, hang from a pendant of diamonds and amethysts of exceptional design. This beautiful ornament is part of a set; the matching ring is shown on the book's cover. Marchak, *Paris.*

XIV - Necklace of diamonds and one Grade A round pearl, 12 mm., black with purplish highlights.
Pierre Mourareau, *Tahiti.*

XV - Necklaces made of gold and Poe-Pipi pearls.
Michel Fouchard, *Tahiti.*

XVI - Necklace of Poe-Pipi pearls and diamonds.
Corail, *Tahiti.*

XVII - Earrings from the set shown on page 89, with two Grade A round pearls, 12 mm., one dark, the other light.
Pierre Mourareau, *Tahiti.*

XVIII - Necklace of cream-colored and pink biwa pearls. The centerpiece, paved with diamonds, holds one magnificent Grade A round pearl. The barrettes holding the necklace are encrusted with diamonds.
Polynésie Perles, *Tahiti.*

XIX - Gold necklace of beautiful quality circled pearls with matching bracelet.
The pendant is a Grade A pear-shaped pearl, 12.4 mm., of the greenish black color known as "Poe-Rava."
"Perle" Jewelers, *Tahiti.*

XX - Hina wearing a necklace of gold and "keshis" youthful and charming.
Michel Fouchard, *Tahiti.*

XXI - An extraordinary creation that marries black and white pearls in perfect harmony.
Giovanni Onorato, *Milan.*

XXII - A fabulous necklace, worthy of Scherezade, displaying diamonds, rubies and gold, underlined by nine pear-shaped black pearls. Nearly a thousand hours of work is required to create such a masterpiece.
Giovanni Onorato, *Milan.*

XXIII - A magnificent confection of black pearls, gold, and diamonds where the talent of the jeweler reaches that of the sculptor.
Giovanni Onorato, *Milan.*

XXIV - Closeup of the necklace shown on facing page.

XXV - Two necklaces: one of baroque pearls on a hand-worked gold chain, the other of black pearls from Tahiti combined with white pearls from Japan.
Pierre Mourareau, *Tahiti.*

JEAN-PAUL LINTILHAC, M.D.

Dr. Lintilhac, a world-famous cosmetic surgeon, is also the author of a book on cosmetic surgery.

In the middle 70's, at the peak of his career, with a very successful practice in Paris, he made the decision to turn his back on the hurly-burly of city life. He knew Polynesia, having traveled there regularly since 1962. In 1975 he moved to Tahiti and opened the clinic where he now practices.

A frequent visitor to Manihi atoll, he found himself drawn to black pearls and fascinated with the biology of the pearl oyster. Later, his interest extended to the installation and development of two pearl farms which afforded him an insider's view of all stages of the production of pearls and the way they are marketed.

This book is the result: a well-researched study that bears the hallmark of Dr. Lintilhac's solid, practical experience in the field.

ALAIN DURAND

Trained as a biologist, with the French Licence* and a Diploma of Advanced Studies, Alain Durand is first and foremost a lover of art and nature — and of the two combined. To him, nature is art. His life is a storybook of adventure — a jungle where he delights in discovery and breaks new trails with respect. Photography is part and parcel of his being.

In journalism he found a practical application for his talents. For more than ten years he was with *Photo-Cinéma* magazine. He contributed photographs to various books, among them *A Guide to the Tarn* by Jean Roques.

In 1971 Durand's book on *Photo-Cine Macrography* (Paul Montel, Publisher), combining as it did his artistic gifts with his mastery of photographic technique, made him an acknowledged authority in his field. The book is in its fifth edition with 100,000 copies in print. With the sky now the limit, Durand broke away and went to Tahiti, where he lived for six years (1974-1980). In the *Guide Bleus* series, published by Hachette, he brought out *Visa* and *Tahiti, Polynesia, Easter Island.*

In 1980 another turn in the road took him to Rome. In Italy, where art is a religion and passion still can be expressed without restraint, he published his first book of photographic art, *Living in Tahiti and Polynesia* (Massimo Baldini, Milan, and Menges, Paris, co-publishers). The photographs from this book were featured on National Italian Television (RAI) on a Raffaella Carra telecast known as *Pronto Raffaella. The Black Pearls of Tahiti* marks another stage in the brilliant career of this author/photographer whose sights are already set on new projects.

---

* *The equivalent of a Ph.D.*

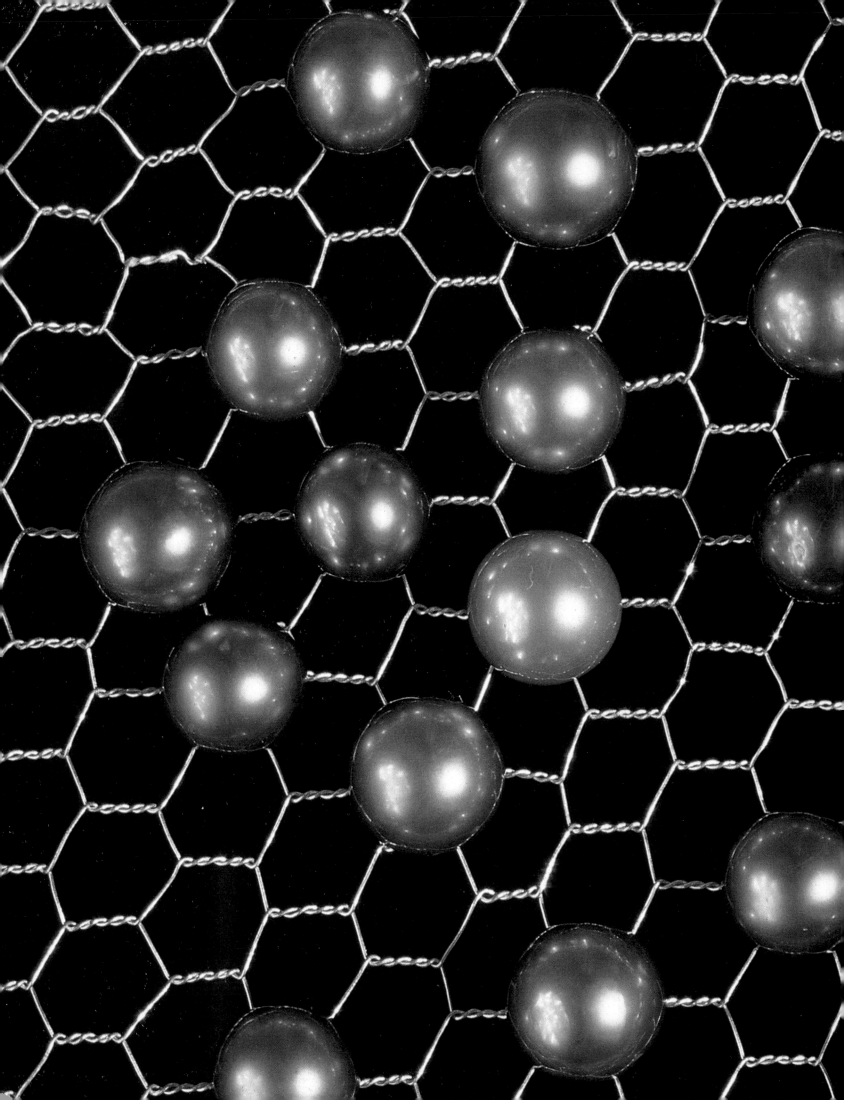